On Bodies: An Anthology

3 of Cups Press

Published in 2018 by
3 of Cups Press
London

Paperback ISBN 978 1 99987 763 7

Printed and bound by CPI Group (UK) Ltd, Croydon, CR0 4YY
Cover design by Harriet Smelt & Clare Bogen

www.3ofcups.co.uk

Introduction

On Bodies was always planned to be the book that followed *On Anxiety*. It seemed fitting to go from the anxiety-inducing political, economic and social climate of 2017 to the myriad ways those conflicts played out across our bodies. We at 3 of Cups Press thoroughly subscribe to the old adage that to best understand someone is to figuratively walk a mile in their shoes, and we all envisioned On Bodies as not only a tremendous literary selection, but also an opportunity for readers to learn about other ways of living, of being and existing.

Each person's relationship to their own body is unique, influenced by the world around us, the culture and society we grow up in, and our genetics and life experiences. As a disabled person, I have a complex relationship with my own skin and bones and everything in between, further complicated by the reality of living as a disabled person in a world actively hostile to differences beyond the straight, white and male.

In this collection, we wanted to showcase that diversity of experience and how people navigate a world not built with them in mind. Inside these pages you will find stories of desire, rejection, pain, triumph, laughter, and the determination to keep going. I had the immense pleasure of being the first editor to read the book cover to cover, and I am incredibly proud of the work our artists and the editorial team have created.

As ever, thank you to everyone who made this book possible: from Kickstarter pledges to preorders, tweets, and nudging emails sent around friends and family -- every moment of support has helped us to bring this book to life. Special thanks go to our contributors, who have explored some incredibly difficult and personal topics with a wealth of creativity, insight and talent. And so, over to them.

Lizzie Huxley-Jones
3 of Cups Press

Contents

Rebecca Thursten

8

Dress Like a Woman
Kiran Millwood Hargrave

I used to be a field riotous with flowers.
I took up space so magnificently,
visitors would tread as soft as snails
trailing their wet worship across
every tender blade of grass, leaving offerings
heaped at my boundaries, or placed
over my soil-reeking heart –

they took nothing I did not give happily
from my blossom shedding fingers,
my hive alive mouth. I could open or close
at will, kiss honey or bite stings and always
my body rolled outwards
building across sky-wide hills –

and now? My mouth is a trapdoor
heaped with dirt. They come with shovels
to force each of my teeth
until I spit bone seeds. Split open and raw
dressed in simple skin they make sure I know
I am not more.

When I say I remember fresh rain on my breath
they tell me I reek.
When I hear rivers tracing the pulse of my blood
they tell me I'm damned.
When I feel lightning sing its hymn between my thighs
or streak through the fillings of my teeth
or begin to burn the soles of my feet
they tell me light and heat is sin
and I must open only to them.

And everywhere they turn us to face each other
and say *watch how she does it.*
Watch how she makes a silence of herself.

9

And through her half-open mouth
I see flashes of sky and stars and know
she has wrapped her insides in storms
trapped oceans under her tongue
and along my gum line rises a tide
and against my molars
                    I taste salt.

On Choice, at Home and Abroad

Ana Kinsella

[Content note: abortion, rape]

[Editor's note: This piece was written before the 25 May 2018 referendum in Ireland. The author of this piece donated her fee to a charity campaigning for the repeal of the Eighth Amendment. However, despite the win, worldwide abortion rights are never truly safe. Take, for example, the United States. This year (2018) marks 45 years since the landmark Roe v. Wade abortion rights case. Since then, 12,000 state laws have been enacted to restrict abortion. The current Vice President Mike Pence has said that abortion will 'end' in our time in the United States. He is also a proponent of a particularly cruel act of legislation that would require people to bury their miscarried foetuses. Throughout the United States, clinics are shutting down, forcing people to travel across or out of state for a termination. Often, this is impossible for financial or logistical reasons. Restrictions such as these are akin to forcing people to give birth. Even where abortion is decriminalised, misogynistic government policies insure terminations remain out of reach for the poorest and most marginalised of us.]

It is impossible to pinpoint a single moment in the struggle for reproductive rights in Ireland, or to reduce it to a simple potted history. For more than my lifetime, the uterus has been a battleground.

In 1983, the Eighth Amendment of the Irish Constitution was passed by referendum, ensuring constitutional recognition of the right to life of the unborn as equal to that of the mother. Coming in the wake of the verdict of Roe v. Wade in the United States, this amendment effectively banned abortion across the Irish Republic.[1]

In January 1984, a schoolgirl named Ann Lovett gave birth in a church grotto in her hometown of Granard in the

1   In 2018, Ireland held a referendum on repealing this amendment. It passed 66.4% to 33.6%.

11

Irish midlands. She was fifteen. Both she and her baby died.

When I was growing up, stories like Ann's were kept as relics of an older Ireland. They signified corruption and silence. In the present day, we simply exported tragedy, on the ferries and Ryanair flights that took people in crisis to England to access safe and legal abortion there. And for many people, the silence was what continued. The silence that surrounded the delicate, thorny issue of what it was to be a woman in a country governed by Catholic laws – that is, to be fallible and human and subject always to tragedy and shame.

In many corners of the country, a crisis pregnancy or one out of wedlock was a source of shame. The news of Ann Lovett's death represented a chance for many others to share their similar stories for the first time. People in these situations were often sent to mother and baby homes or to relatives in England until the pregnancy came to term. And with that shame came silence. The two work together to paralyse and to suffocate. Together, the two can be fatal.

In the days after Ann Lovett's death, during her reporting on the ground, the journalist Nell McCafferty wrote in her report for *In Dublin* magazine: 'So long as the family kept silent, the community honoured the unwritten code of non-interference with the basic unit of society.' The belief, according to the townspeople and the parish priest, was that nobody had known Ann was pregnant. The silence that ensued contributed to the circumstances of her death.

'Had a teenage boy been found dying from whatever cause,' McCafferty wrote, 'no one would have balked at an inquiry. You don't walk away from a male youth, found dying in a grotto that celebrates the Virgin Birth.'

Seven years later, a fourteen-year-old girl was raped by a man close to her family. She became pregnant and during the ensuing investigation, elected to travel with her family to the UK to seek a termination. On the date of travel, the Attorney General filed an injunction to prevent them doing so, based principally on the Eighth Amendment. The family returned and quickly a clinical psychologist found that the girl had become suicidal. The case was brought to the Supreme Court,

12

with an appeal on the behalf of the girl, known as X, that centred on the equal right to life of the mother. The judge ruled in her favour, and she was ultimately permitted to travel. The X case spurred on more debate about the topic, leading to a referendum in 1992 that allowed both the freedom to travel to access abortion, and the freedom to share information on accessing abortion.

When I was growing up in Ireland, these incidents loomed but they seemed to have happened elsewhere, in an Ireland that was still in black and white and governed only by the Church. They were difficult to talk about, and so they often happened on the news, delivered in terse, straightforward language that did not do justice to the content. They were difficult to talk about, and so many people didn't, really. For my whole lifetime the problem of unplanned or unwanted pregnancy has been exported. The statistics have been laid bare: eleven or twelve women travel from Ireland to the UK every single day to access abortion. Many more order pills online and take them alone and without medical supervision. It took a long time to learn this, because silence prevents us from seeing the truth.

And it took me a lot longer to realise that trauma, grief, silence and shame can linger across society. This was a country where people were forced to experience violence and trauma in silence and in secrecy, lest it damage the power structures that already ruled Irish society. As long as Irish people have to board planes and boats to access full medical care, it still is.

It's important to note how the role of sharing stories, of opening up and talking about our experiences, has been so fundamental in the current push for change. One example is the work of a group called Termination for Medical Reasons – a group of people and their partners who, usually after the diagnosis of fatal foetal abnormalities, have had to travel from Ireland to the UK to terminate their pregnancies on medical grounds. Often these pregnancies won't survive outside the womb. The importance of the stories these people have shared – stories of heartbreak and agony over much-longed-for babies, but also of unexpected generosity and care

13

from Liverpool taxi drivers or medical professionals – can't be understated. Personal stories and the collective freedom to tell them have taken the issue from something that happens to other people, behind closed doors, to something tangible across the board. It happens on your street. It can happen to anyone.

It's strange now to say how much the sharing of these often traumatic stories could feel at times like a balm. Opening up, talking to friends about their own experiences, examining how Ireland had treated women over the years – it felt like a way to combat shame and silence.

And yet there is still a dislocation inherent in having a uterus in Ireland. This is your home, and yet it only wants you under certain circumstances, in certain formations. This is your body, and yet it exists under someone else's rule – a line in the Constitution that nobody born after 1965 has had a chance to vote on until this year. The uterus has always been contested ground. So who has a right to claim it?

Ireland's recent battle was primarily a legal one, that enabled people to access the vital medical care they need and deserve. That legal battle has been fought by people up and down the country, lifelong campaigners and those who simply joined a canvass or wore a badge this year. And the law itself can be changed in a day. But there is another battle that lies behind every struggle for reproductive rights around the world: the battle for equality is one that determines who gets to speak, to tell stories, to drive a narrative. For decades in Ireland a veil of silence was pulled around the lives of women. It is only now that this has been able to lift.

In her recent autobiographical novel *Motherhood*, Sheila Heti writes:

> *When I think of all the people who want to forbid abortions, it seems it can only mean one thing – not that they want this new person in the world, but that they want that woman to be doing the work of childrearing more than they want her to be doing anything else. There's*

14

*something threatening about a woman who is
not occupied with children. There is something
at-loose-ends feeling about such a woman. What
is she going to do instead? What sort of trouble
will she make?*[2]

A woman with a voice is a dangerous thing. A woman
with choice, with autonomy, perhaps even more so. The work
done by activists and campaigners and ordinary people of all
genders across the country in recent years has shifted the narrative. Their work must be honoured and we owe them an
incredible debt. But there is also work for everyone to do.
The Ireland handed to our childrens' generation should be
one without shame, without guilt, without silence. We need
to free ourselves from these things – we can't live fully until
we do.

And this does not start and end with Ireland, of course. It's
easy for people in more liberal countries to look at particular
cases – whether it be a controversial court case in Brazil, or
the country of Ireland itself – as flashpoints or anomalies, dark
spots that show up on an X-ray and can terrify. But around
the world, in every country, people with uteri remain at risk.
Bodily autonomy has been a hard-won thing and that must
never be taken for granted. And this is not just something
that happens far away. Anti-abortion sentiment is growing in
Britain today, and the issue is still vital in Northern Ireland,
which is the only part of the United Kingdom where abortion
is still illegal in the vast majority of circumstances. After the
Irish referendum, attention will turn to the North. But the law
there can be changed from Westminster, if the UK government
chooses to do so. So far, Prime Minister Theresa May has
deflected the issue, saying it is a local matter for the devolved
Northern Ireland executive. And as seen from debates around
Planned Parenthood in the United States, progress can never
be written off as a given. Choice must be fought for and pre-
served and always protected, because none of us can be free
without it.

2   Sheila Heti, *Motherhood*. (London: Harvill Secker, 2018), p. 29.

Walking
Alice Tarbuck

Able-bodied as I am, I have always walked. From my first totters down the garden path, to scaling sizeable Munros at the age of nine. For me, walking was not a joy, per se. It wasn't something I paid any attention to at all.

Walking changed for me, dramatically, with the commencement of my chronic illness at the age of twenty-one. For several years, my illness made walking painful, and on some days almost impossible. Every effort of walking had to be measured with its reward, and walking for pleasure was eliminated. Now, with good management, I am able to walk again, and mostly you would never know that I had undergone a period of limited mobility.

But I am still a nervous walker: I attempt to work out how far away things are, and plot alternative transport in case I get halfway and have to stop walking. Mountains, then, are somewhat out of reach. I've walked in foothills, walks of an hour or so, but that exhilarating eight-hour journey, from base to summit, laden with sandwiches and vigour, eludes me. I miss it. It feels as if a significant way of engaging with the natural world has been taken from me. Walking in nature looms large in the British imagination. The natural world is healing, we hear, and immersion in it is good for us. Not only that, but it is fundamentally part of our identity; the land we walk on, the countryside around us. Feeling divorced from that, as someone who keenly loves the natural world, is difficult.

Walking is, of course, mostly unremarkable – simply one of many ways of getting from place to place. However, it transforms when taken from that context and placed into one of leisure, of walking as part of the larger idea of engagement with the natural world. Indeed, such walking has recently come under investigation, been made the central topic of conferences and papers. Certainly, walking continues to provide a rich and compelling topic of analysis. Walking has been discussed in every possible manifestation: as artistic practice; mode of ecological engagement; 'inexpensive recreation'. However, walking has an opposite, an inability to walk, and an encounter with the limitations of one's body. That is what has been largely written out of the history of walking, out of considerations of its cultural and social importance.

Walking was elevated to an art, a feat of daring, by the advent of serious mountaineering concomitant with the Romantic period and the development of the concept of the sublime. Robert Macfarlane, in his book on the history of mountain climbing, *Mountains of the Mind*, writes that:

> risk-taking brings with it its own reward: it keeps a "continual agitation alive" in the heart. … Life, it frequently seems in the mountains, is more intensely lived the closer one gets to its extinction: we never feel so alive as when we have nearly died.[1]

The extremities of walking, then, bring us close to death, close to heights that others have not reached, things unknown to most mere mortals. Walking, that most human of pursuits, literally elevates man above his peers, discloses to him knowledge of inaccessible places, allows him to overcome the challenge of the landscape. Mountains, used to navigate by from the populate lowlands, become what Rebecca Solnit calls 'unearthly earth', places not historically ventured into. To walk up mountains is to conquer, is to elevate walking to a higher plane.[2]

Although walking, and the freedom to move through the landscape generally, has been the preserve of men, walking is also, as Rebecca Solnit notes, a vital denotation of independence for women:

> For [Jane Austen and the readers of Pride and Prejudice], as for Mr. Darcy, [Elizabeth Ben-

1   Robert Macfarlane, *Mountains of the Mind* (London: Granta, 2017), p. 37.

2   Rebecca Solnit, *Wanderlust*, (London: Granta, 2014), p. 69.

18

net's] solitary walks express the independence
that literally takes the heroine out of the social
sphere of the houses and their inhabitants, into
a larger, lonelier world where she is free to think:
walking articulates both physical and mental
freedom.[3]

Walking, for Austen's characters, literally removes them from the sphere of social scrutiny and facilitates the development of independent thought, and because it does so, it becomes a marker of difference. Women who walk are seen as dangerous, as less entrapped within a social web designed to subjugate their will. Women who walk take risks, may have encounters which are not socially sanctioned whilst in the landscape. Walking, here, is an activity of self-fashioning, one that allows space for the self to come into being, removed from social pressure.

What, then, of those who cannot conquer mountains, or don their bonnets and stride out across the hills? Are they destined to remain corralled within society, unable to escape? Are they confined to a life without truly experiencing landscape, without participating in these natural spaces which, as Macfarlane and Solnit establish, seem so crucial in forming identity and bonds with our world?

The answer is complicated and largely unsatisfactory. When I was unable to walk long distances, I felt extremely divorced from the natural world as I had traditionally understood it, and I felt disbarred from accessing it, as if I no longer qualified for participation. The dominant narratives around walking seemed to relate to conquest and the glory of the lone traveller, tramping miles across the landscape.

However, there was one walking writer whose work I turned to during that period of limited mobility: Nan Shepherd (1893–1981). Nan Shepherd is the author of a number of novels which centre on the relationship between culture and the natural world in turn-of-the-century North East Scotland. She is also the author of a non-fiction work, *The*

3   Rebecca Solnit, *Wanderlust*, (London: Granta, 2014), p. 69.

Living Mountain, an extraordinary book that explores Shepherd's lifelong relationship with the Cairngorm Mountains. Although Shepherd is writing at the same time that masculine pursuits such as mountaineering are extremely popular she puts forward radical new ways of reading and understanding landscape. The book was written during the 1940s, and Shepherd sent it off for consideration by her friend, the writer Neil Gunn, but despite his enthusiasm for it, the book was not published until 1977. The result of this was that Shepherd was very much absent from conceptions of the modernist canon, and thus largely overlooked until relatively recently.

Shepherd's work on her lifelong friendship with the Cairngorms, that forbidding range of mountains, might seem an odd choice of lifeline for a person who could not walk. But Shepherd, although she celebrates the vast spaces of the mountains, does not lionise walking as an end in itself. The important thing, for her, is not the miles walked, the exhilaration of reaching the summit, the feeling of having conquered something. Rather, Shepherd understands walking as a means of facilitating other forms of sensory engagement with the world. Shepherd seeks to de-centre the ascent of mountains as their primary attraction, referring to her engagement with the Cairngorms as 'a meditation not a manifesto … a pilgrimage and not an attack'.[4] Shepherd is interested in the 'essential nature' of the mountain: in understanding it from all angles and in all seasons. Most importantly, perhaps, Shepherd is interested in understanding the mountain from every possible angle. She swims in the lochs, feels grass under her bare feet, the hardness of rocks, the heat of the sun. She celebrates the skin as an organ of exploration, and touch as a powerful means of understanding the world:

> *The whole skin has this delightful sensitivity; it feels the sun, it feels the wind running inside one's garment, it feels water closing on it as one slips under … This plunge into the cold water of a mountain pool seems*

4   Nan Shepherd, *The Living Mountain,* (Edinburgh: Canongate, 2011), p. 103.

for a brief moment to disintegrate the very self.[5]

Rather than measuring distance covered or feet climbed, Shepherd measures her time in the hills through a broad range of bodily experience. Not only does Shepherd engage with the weather, she also participates in the landscape in non-walking ways, by swimming, feeling the cold mountain water against her skin. To feel the sun or the wind, or indeed to feel cold water: these activities do not require athletic prowess. They do not even require an able body. Instead, these are activities which can be done in any open space, especially one with water, or where it is raining. Her experience with water, Shepherd states, is that it seems to 'dissolve the self'. Through her interactions with the meteorological forces around her, and the composite elements that make up landscape, Shepherd is able to relate the landscape to herself, and in turn distribute her perception through the landscape imaginatively rather than maintaining an embodied, anthropocentric viewpoint.

By refusing to honour the traditional separations between land and self, Shepherd removes the primacy of walking from encounters with landscape. Instead, Shepherd suggests other ways of interacting with the landscape, which can be achieved by those who cannot so easily scale mountains. During the period where my mobility was very limited, I started going into the garden, down the stone stairs in my parents' house, and sitting in a chair at the bottom of the stairs. Then, often wrapped in a blanket, I'd wait to see what happened. There was always something. A robin in the bushes. A sudden gust of wind that set the maple tree rattling. A cat, one of the many in the street, running through the garden in hot pursuit of a squirrel it would never catch. The squawk of a magpie. The coo-coo of a pigeon, jauntily saluting me from the ivy. These things, which I had so often walked past, walked through, been too fast for, suddenly became small moments of comfort. I would keep them; catalogue them, to tell my mum when she got home, or to write to my partner in emails. Because my

5   Nan Shepherd, *The Living Mountain,* (Edinburgh: Canongate, 2011), p. 103.

21

world had become very small, and I barely left the house unless it was in the car, the garden had become my Cairngorms, the pond my loch, the lawn my great green expanse. I learned that even the smallest observable alteration in the world, a new bud, or the falling of a leaf, can hold enormous joy and give a sense of the greatness of the world, without having to tower over it from a mountain top or walk miles over its surface. The garden didn't mind that I couldn't walk. Indeed, the stillness is what permitted the land to disclose itself to me, and for me to witness it.

There is magic in allowing the natural world to show itself to you, without having to 'conquer' it. There is magic to de-centering walking as an experience, and getting rid of snobbishness about 'wilderness' and the unique glory of hard-to-reach spots on cliffs and peaks. The ordinary world is just as full of wonders. Emma Mitchell, who has written a book on the relationship between the natural world and mental health, *Making Winter*, writes that 'simply being in green spaces can alter levels of mood boosting neurotransmitters'.[6] Whilst walking certainly has benefits to cardiovascular health, it is not the only health-boosting way to interact with the natural world, as Mitchell argues. Instead, she suggests a range of nature-adjacent activities such as preserving leaves and making nature tables. When I became ill, I hadn't made a nature table since I was a child. It was an activity exclusively for children, I thought, or perhaps for serious foragers, displaying their trays of unusual mushrooms. But when I began my short forays outside, it made me enormously happy to return with treasures. Fallen leaves, feathers, the seedpods of interesting plants, and flowers for pressing. By bringing these things into my house, by drying and arranging them, I was able to immerse myself in the natural world even when I was in too much pain to make it into the garden. Leaves, twigs, little snail shells: these are all important reminders that the world we live in is wide and vast, and that it held in it far more than simply my pain and limitations. The mountains

6   Emma Mitchell, *Making Winter: A Creative Guide for Surviving the Winter Months* (London: LOM Art, 2017), p. 12

might have been distant, but the natural world could remain close.

The Scottish poet Alec Finlay has done a great deal of work to refigure ideas of walking for those less able to access the distant mountains, and to bring them closer. Finlay suffers from ME, and is often indisposed. He writes: 'I know the feeling well – worried by distance ... Whenever I go for a walk I calculate the likely effect, based on incline and terrain ... I can rest in pain at home.'[7] Finlay references Nan Shepherd's style of walking as inspirational to his own: 'sometimes I refer to my anti-summitism – mountains are there to walk in and around, as Nan Shepherd said, as well as up.'[8] This practice, of finding other ways to experience the landscape which do not privilege the legs, he refers to as 'The New Walking'.[9] Finlay describes ways in which we might re-frame and re-imagine walking as an inclusive experience: 'We can walk imaginatively. We may have to – through illness, age, confinement dispossession, limits imposed on the right to roam, even imprisonment ... [Walking] exists on a spectrum running from the purely physical to the purely imaginative.'[10] This 'imaginative walking' is represented in Finlay's art practice by the use of labels. These labels make a small poem out of the names of hills and mountains, and are then photographed against the backdrop of the mountain from a low-lying position.

By naming the mountains, by labelling them, Finlay is engaging with them on a textual level. By writing poems about them, Finlay is enacting the idea of the imaginative walk, by exploring the mountains using something other than walking. Just as Shepherd uses her body to explore the natural world in ways other than on foot, so Finlay uses imaginative play to assert a non-physical relationship with the natural world. This labelling felt revelatory for me. I've never been much

7   Alec Finlay 'Invisible Barriers' (Edinburgh: John Muir Trust, 2017) <www.johnmuirtrust.org/about/resources/1281-invisible-barriers>

8   Ibid.

9   Alec Finlay, 'Upper Teviot, A Note on Place-names', (Edinburgh: Alec Finlay Blog, 2017)

10   Ibid.

good at sketching, but I have learned to love sitting with a view of the hills, inside or outside, and sketching out poems. I have found such joy in the detail that a pair of binoculars affords, tracking my friends up a mountain, or spotting a lone deer high on a slope. I have given myself permission for this to be enough, for this to be a legitimate way of engaging with the natural world. Out of this practice have come a number of poems, and also a deep sense of satisfaction. If I can avoid the long walks, I'm less likely to have flare-ups that make the short walks impossible. Now, I feel I've found a way to achieve that, whilst not feeling a deep sense of sadness for the limitations of my body.

I am comparatively lucky, in that my ability to be mobile comes and goes. I know that access to the natural world is even more limited for wheelchair users, or those with other mobility issues. There are a huge number of ableist, classist and racist barriers to equal participation in the natural world, and indeed in navigating space at all. This essay does not seek to suggest that I hold any answers. However, this is a reflection on the ways of responding to my body in its strangeness, in its relapsing-and-remitting difficulty. The world feels un-tethered, difficult, strange, when your body ceases to behave in the way you'd come to take for granted. It has been difficult to re-learn the idea of the natural world, and how I might relate to it. In small ways, on shorter walks and in different spaces, I have learnt to look more closely, listen more closely, feel things on my skin, collect things to look at later. These small excursions and small experiences let me dwell happily in this strange body, and let me shape myself in relation to the natural world. They help my body be a body in the world, in a way that makes sense for me.

On Touch: the Desexualisation of Black Women's Bodies

Stephanie Phillips

Leaning forward from my friend's sofa, I picked up a pitcher of rum punch from a makeshift table in the centre of a circle of women. As I poured myself another cooling glass of punch, I briefly dipped below the animated conversation that floated over my head, until I brought myself back to the group.

The cheered, ecstatic voices of the black women around me unified as one, echoing one another's take on everything from Solange's new single to the latest political catastrophe of the day. On a warm summer's afternoon, we sipped well, ate well and laughed well. News of a date I had later that evening was met with wild curiosity from the group. Who were they? What are they like? Curiosity to which I sadly could not appease as websites such as OkCupid often encourage users to withhold information.

Talk about various love interests led to further dissection of our dating history and then, naturally, our sex lives. In most women-oriented films, this is the point where the group of girlfriends jovially laugh about the multitude of ways they love to have sex, bonding over their voracious and healthy love of intimacy. This isn't a film. This is real life and in one of a number of ways black women's lives often differ from white women's. Our conversation did not follow that well-trodden path. Instead, we rather reflected on the ways we either felt scared or disconnected from our bodies and sexualities. Why did many of us wait years until we had sex? Why do we struggle to vocalise our needs?

We were all women from vastly different backgrounds, who embodied the dictionary definition of black girl magic in every other part of our lives. We were confident, stylish, intelligent. So, why were we plagued with doubt? These revelations clustered in the air as the sun began to set. I took another sip of punch, reflecting on the weight of the shared experience we acknowledged.

Years later, I still wonder why this experience, so familiar to black women, is rarely discussed. The hyper-sexualisation of black women's bodies (where black women are seen as overtly sexual, promiscuous and predatory) is a well-known term. What is rarely talked about, however, is the counter-effect of hyper-sexualisation: the desexualisation of black women's bodies. Black women are often seen as a mammy (a sexless mothering figure) whose wants and needs are regularly overlooked. Black women's bodies are also often positioned as the direct opposite of what is deemed beautiful (light skin, straight hair, Caucasian features). Often, we are only called beautiful when we embody aspects of those features.

Both sexualised and desexualised stereotypes are unhealthy caricatures created for and because of the male gaze. Either state fails to consider what black women want in their sex lives: that black women may have sex for themselves rather than to please others. The ground-breaking self-help book *Sisters of the Yam* by bell hooks shines a light on the limitations of hyper-sexualisation and desexualisation. hooks claims that in societies where black women's bodies are objectified and dehumanised daily, it is difficult for them to find power in their own erotic sexuality:

> *Many black females learn early on how to objectify themselves, their bodies, and use their sexuality as a commodity that can be exchanged in the sexual marketplace. The black women who have internalized this way of thinking about their sexual selves, though may appear 'liberated', are in actuality completely estranged from their erotic powers. Their estrangement is just as intense as that of black females who have learned from childhood on that they can protect themselves from objectification, from commodification by repressing erotic energy, by denying any sensual or sexual dimension in themselves.*[1]

1   bell hooks, Sisters of the Yam: Black Women and Self Recovery (New York: South End Press, 1994), p. 87.

hooks argues, as black women, we are unconsciously denying ourselves the chance to connect with 'erotic energy' as a way to survive in a society which hooks herself has called the 'imperialist, white supremacist, capitalist patriarchy'. The thought that sexism and racism affects me, even in privacy, is a bitter pill to swallow. Have I been unaware of the ways I've been denying myself love by trying to fit in? I think back to times where I've been glad to be ignored by leering workmen on building sites. The men gathered around rickety scaffolding, lips pursed ready to whistle and yelp at the next woman they deem 'sexy'. They generally leave me alone. I have avoided the trouble of unpacking sex and sexuality in favour of having an easier life, but what life am I leading if I am not living life to its fullest?

Coming to terms with my relationship with my own body is something I've always put off. I'm a 29-year-old woman, with one serious relationship and a decent family life that has kept me stable. It feels almost embarrassing to admit that I still don't really know what I want from sex, or who I am in terms of my relationship to my body.

From day to day, my view on my body changes. I'll catch a glimpse of myself in the mirror one day and become enamoured with the brilliance of my rich skin or the curve of my hips. At other times, I only notice the disjointed symmetry of my face or the extra pounds I've gained over the years.

This is not to say I've never felt sexy, but perhaps it was always on someone else's terms. As a shy person who has often felt overlooked, I accepted what little attention I occasionally received. I did this rather than attempt to learn more about myself and, as bell hooks says in *Sisters of the Yam*, 'create spaces of pleasure' in my life.

To feel disconnected from my body in my twenties makes me feel removed from society. When people talk about the thrills of being sex positive, of polyamorous relationships, or the highs and lows of the dating world, I never know what to say. My lack of experience in these situations often makes me feel less than. As if I am not pulling my weight because I cannot make that connection within myself.

27

I would be perfectly content knowing I felt this way if it was something I actually wanted but I don't. I want to show someone I love them and be loved back. The root of my issues could also stem from my battle with touch. Signalling that I need affection is a skill I have struggled to master. When friends meet me, they often hesitate to hug me. Their arms hang with uncertainty in mid-air as my body language suggests I want anything but connection. In reality I yearn for touch and connection but making that translate is a hurdle I have not yet managed to confront.

Maybe my hard exterior was ingrained in me through my family's stoic nature, even if they are by nature loving and also forgiving. As an 11-year-old child, my father was sent from Jamaica to England alone on a plane without knowing why or where he was going. No malice played a part in my great-grandparents' decision, but often, practicality is given more gravitas than emotional wellbeing in Caribbean families. They were mostly likely devastated to lose my father, but yet, they decided this was the best option, perhaps without considering his needs and wishes.

On the other hand, my mother is someone who hugs others. She has to remind me to hug her every time I visit. It's a simple task many do without hesitation. I consider the ways she has influenced me and my relationships. When I thank her for helping me out she simply replies 'of course I would do that, what did you expect me to do?' Again, practicality overrides emotion. I relayed this story to a friend once who pointed out I do exactly the same thing.

Recognising and correcting the multitude of ways I deny myself touch is a step forward in dealing with my fears. When I talk to people, I lean in, make eye contact. I think of mantras to repeat to myself in the mirror, but sometimes all I can think of is RuPaul: 'if you can't love yourself how in the hell are you going to love anybody else?'

Stepping forward and declaring the importance of touch and connection is a first attempt at incorporating the sensual into my sexuality. Being truly in tune with your needs has to go beyond the limits of simple physical pleasure. It must transform into something more. Correcting society's negative brainwashing and rhetoric can improve more than just your personal pleasure. In *Uses of the Erotic*, Audre Lorde discusses how tuning into your body's needs is a radical act in itself:

> *Recognising the power of the erotic within our lives can give us the energy to pursue genuine change within our world, rather than merely settling for a shift of characters in the same weary drama. For not only do we touch our most profoundly creative source, but we do that which is female and self-affirming in the face of a racist, patriarchal, and anti-erotic society.*[2]

This leads me to the crux of my reasoning for wanting change in my sex life and how I knew a standard *Cosmopolitan* article wouldn't solve anything. Rather than just experiencing physical pleasure, real agency comes from knowing what you want, what you deserve and what you refuse to tolerate. In every other area of my life I try and uphold this mantra knowing that every time I stand up for myself the patriarchy loses. I wouldn't let a work colleague deny me my humanity, so why should I let a potential partner? Finding your own version of sensuality can help in your understanding of yourself and therefore help fight against an intrinsically racist, sexual, heteronormative society.

Going forward, I realise I have the tools and knowledge to fight back against the racist, sexist brainwashing that has altered my view of my sexuality, and in turn, my own body. I'm ready for what comes next: to feel, to love, to finally touch with feeling.

2   Audre Lorde, 'Uses of the Erotic: The Erotic as Power', *Sister Outsider: Essays and Speeches* (Berkeley: Ten Speed Press, 1984).

Sanatana Dharma: Finding My Place in My Body

Krish Jeyakumar

In English, there is no singular, widely recognised word for the opposite of having a gender, or the opposite of a binary. If there was, I think that's what I'd want to be called.

Gender has never been a thing I've wanted to label. Or rather, that was how I felt until I discovered my culture. Every step I take further into exploring Hinduism and my relationship with the Gods is a balm that soothes wounds born from trying to change my body into something more socially acceptable.

The more time I've spent looking into Hinduism, the more I'm able to understand that my body enables me to do everything. My body takes up room. My body cooks new meals, discovering the miracle of properly seasoned water whilst getting food stains all over my recipe notebook. My body lays my head in my mum's lap and listens to stories of my grandparents who I never got the chance to meet. My body allows me to leaf through books and transcripts and scripture and discover things about my culture that I never knew before.

My interest in Hinduism was reignited at university. In second year, I took a course on Norse mythology and was tasked with comparing the pantheon of Gods/stories to another, and I chose Hinduism. The Valkyries to the Palchara and Apsaras; Freyja and Kali; Odin and Shiva; Yama and Hel. I was so interested to see how civilisations on either side of the world still managed to create such a similar pantheon. However, my essay was disregarded by my white American professor, who didn't recognise the scripture I cited as an accurate source, insisting I include more academic proof. When I defended my work, explaining this comparison hadn't been deeply studied before, I was told '[i] should've picked a more popular subject then, maybe a Marvel movie?' I was absolutely furious at the way I had been brushed off, but this interaction reignited my fire for exploring Hinduism in more depth.

The first time I understood Brahma was the first time that I understood what familiarity felt like. The first time I read about Ardhanarishvara was the first time that I thought *I'm allowed to keep my culture and be myself*. The first time I discovered Kali Amman was the first time I felt that I could be proud of my relationship with gender.

A good place to start is with our understanding of reality. Brahma is the personification of all that is material, efficient and final in existence. In Vedic scripture their name comes from the root *bṛh-*, meaning 'to be or make firm, strong, solid, expand, promote'. The primary focus of the early Upanishads[1] is Brahmavidya and Atmavidya, which is the study of Brahma and Atman, essentially the knowledge of the self and soul.

With a grammatically genderless presence in the scriptures, Brahma, the ultimate divine, is beyond our mortal differentiations of sex. There are no limitations or inhibitions to their being. Unlike a lot of monotheistic religions[2], the presence of Brahma shows a being who rules the cosmos whose neutral gender and fluid sexuality intrinsically implies the acceptance of all virtues, genders and dimensions.

Brahma is traditionally depicted with four faces and four arms. Each of Brahma's faces is thought to have uttered one of the Vedas[3], and they each point towards a cardinal direction. Their hands hold no weapons, instead carrying symbols of knowledge and creation. In one hand, they cradle the Vedas. The second holds the mala (similar to rosary beads) symbolising time, in the third there is a ladle (which is used to feed the fire in Hindu temples) and in the last, a kamandalu, a container that holds water, symbolising the beginnings of all life.

1   The Upanishads, a part of the Vedas, are ancient Sanskrit texts that contain some of the central philosophical concepts and ideas of Hinduism, some of which are shared with religious traditions like Buddhism and Jainism.

2   Monotheism literally means 'the belief in only one God'.

3   The Vedas are a large body of knowledge texts originating in the ancient Indian subcontinent. Composed in Vedic Sanskrit, the texts constitute the oldest layer of Sanskrit literature and the oldest scriptures of Hinduism.

Though they are certainly one of the most revered figures in early scripture, Brahma is not actually worshiped often in India and Sri Lanka, compared to the other parts of the holy trinity, because they are not eternal. Whereas other Hindu Gods are seen as immortal, it's widely understood that Brahma will eventually be absorbed into the cosmos one day. This makes them vulnerable, transient and real; a figure who is a lot easier to relate to than an immortal being. A figure who it is almost acceptable to look up to.

Brahma's accepted and grammatically genderless presence in Hinduism felt to me like validation and familiarity when exploring my own gender expression. The fact that they are so wholly loved in scripture and worship and also beyond our mortal ideas of gender meant that there was no reason to feel *wrong*.

In Hindu scripture the unity of opposites is often needed to survive. For example, Brahma's wife, partner and consort is Goddess Saraswati. She is seen as the embodiment of Brahma's power, the way that they harness the creation and energy that drives their actions. She is the opposite of Brahma, balancing out her partner's masculinity with a subtle femininity. These unions can be seen across many of the gods: Sita relates to Rama, Lakshmi to Vishnu, Radha has Krishna, and, perhaps most notably, Shiva and Parvati, who can be seen in their joint form Ardhanarishvara.

Ardhanarishvara is the exploration of the concept that perpetual ecstasy can be reached when you embrace the duality of form. Shiva is one of the holy Hindu trinity, as the god of destruction and transformation, while Parvati is the god of fertility, love and devotion. In pictures, Ardhanarishvara is depicted with one side of their body appearing traditionally masculine and the other traditionally feminine, literal composites of Shiva and Parvati. They represent the amalgam of masculine and feminine energies of the universe and highlight how the male and female principles of God (Shakti and Shiva) are inseparable. In short, totality lies beyond duality.

In their combined physical form we can see many examples of images that relate to the concept of totality beyond duality. The rosary in Ardhanarishvara's depiction associates them with asceticism and the spiritual realm. The mirror that resides on their feminine 'side' represents Parvati's connection with the material world. The combination of the material and the spiritual in Ardhanarishvara reconciles and balances these opposite ways of life (this is also known as *coniunctio oppositorum*, or the unity of opposites, the philosophy of which appears in many schools of thought). They show it is possible to reside in the spiritual realm, whilst still having an anchor in the material world. Simply, you can believe in the bigger picture of the cosmos, and also see importance in the materialistic nature of marriage, a family and household things. To find comfort or be worried about material things isn't a judgement of your character; it is an understanding of totality and layers. Totality being the philosophy of the absolute in Hinduism.

In Ardhanarishvara, I saw that a person could be both masculine and feminine, formidable and gentle, destructive and constructive. They unify all dichotomies. Finding them made me realise that I didn't have to abandon my femininity to prove my gender; I could keep it and still be whole.

In the West, it's expected that we have to conform to the binary, even if you choose to live beyond it. There's a pressure that comes from our concept of androgyny to conform to masculinity. But with Ardhanarishvara I saw that a unity of masculinity and femininity is okay.

With Brahman and Ardhanarishvara by my side, I managed to harness familiarity and balance, but I was still scared. I was scared of my body. Being a fat, brown, ample-chested person in the queer world is terrifying, when it is the skinny, white, flat-chested people with short hair who are considered to be truly androgynous. But Kali taught me not to be afraid of my body. Kali started me on my journey of self love.

Kali comes from the Sanskrit root word *Kal*, which means time. Nothing can escape time, and in this way everyone will have their meeting with Kali eventually. A small aside here, but due to the widely assumed idea that a meeting with 'time' and 'death' are synonymous, many people view Kali as the goddess of death. To an extent this is correct, but you must remember not to use a capital letter when writing the word 'death'. She is not the character 'Death' as imagined in Western faiths, with a hooded cape and a scythe: Kali brings the death of ego and one's self-centred view of reality, not of the body and soul. Yama is the actual god of Death in the Vedas and Hindu scriptures, but Kali's physical form fits a Western idea of a death-bringing deity, causing her to be demonised.

In the Hindu and Vedic scriptures, it is thought that the ego arises out of an obsessive identification with the body. Through this obsession, our journey to Moksha is often elongated as we're not focusing on actions of good karma that will lead us there, but instead are fixating on our physical appearance. Kali is the Hindu form of disregarding an obsession about physicality. Ma Kali dresses in a garland of skulls and skirt of arms, trophies worn by her to symbolise liberating her children from their attachment to the limited body. She holds a sword and a freshly severed head dripping with blood, which represents the great battle in which she destroyed a powerful demon. Her dark skin is the womb of the quantum absolute from which all creation arises and into which all creation will eventually dissolve. She is depicted as standing on Shiva who lays beneath her with white skin (in contrast to her dark skin), with a blissful detached look to show a formless blissful awareness, while she is the form and the eternal substratum of lucid awareness.

Strangely enough, her garland of skulls and skirt of arms were the catalyst for me realising I didn't have to force myself to conform to a mould I couldn't ever possibly fit into. Seeing her wear bodies as decoration made me see that is what they are; simply ornamental. Being able to understand that felt like the most possible, human way of being liberated from bodily obsession. Rather than focusing on the bad things about my body, such as the parts that didn't fit me, I started exploring all the ways that my body helps and protects me.

It is with my body that I am able to be a carer for my parents when they're in ill health. It is through my strength that I can protect myself from racist, homophobic or general aggression. It is with my dexterity that I competitively swam,

35

played table tennis and competed in a basketball league when I was younger. My body lets me listen to music, and feel the cold water around my ankles at the beach. It's the strength in my arms and warmth of my body that lets me hug my friends and hold my partner. And most importantly, it is my body that is the perfect napping spot for my dog.

Life is a learning curve, and with Brahma, Ardhanarishvara and Kali, it feels easier to learn. With their strength within me, I am able to carry myself with a confidence that says 'I belong here, and I deserve this space'. Through Kali, I see that I shouldn't be so scared about how the world sees me. And through Brahma and Ardhanarishvara, I've explored things about myself I didn't know I was allowed to. I have felt comfortable embracing a femininity that I previously thought would invalidate my queerness and I have worn clothes that I used to think would make me stand out too much. With their presence in my life, I feel far more connected to my gender and my relationship with Hinduism. They are my direct link to so much of the culture that got left behind in Sri Lanka when my parents fled. I know that somewhere down the line, somewhere in my ancestry, my family were thinking about themselves like this too.

Natural Remedies
Bryony White

We had decided to take the trip that day because the
warmth in the air was just right. It didn't seem to me that the
weather would matter but Liv insisted it would be crucial to
keep my body temperature up when I was in the water. Liv
had read about the healing qualities particular to the pool we
would visit this afternoon in the local paper. It would be good
for my condition. *It could clear it entirely*, Liv had said whilst
examining the article animatedly. With an eagerness born of
unfaltering optimism in the natural world's ability to soothe
even the most extreme of illnesses or incapacities, Liv con-
cluded that *we should make a trip out of it*. She had always
enjoyed an opportunity to bookend the simplest of activities
with a sense of occasion.

I had read the article too and was moved by the deep,
almost occult, mysticism that seemed somehow incongruent
in a local, community-run newspaper. I definitely didn't take
to the idea of submerging myself in a deep pool of rare geo-
thermal minerals as immediately as Liv did. But she had left
the paper on my bedside table during a visit, tacitly imply-
ing my future readership. It seemed only appropriate that I
avoid the article for at least the first few days, knowing that
this would only enhance Liv's sense of urgency. After a short
while, however, I unfurled the paper's matte front and started
to read. Whilst I quietly appreciated Liv's dedication to the
cause, I had been offered this advice before so continued to
entertain the article with my usual scepticism of the mystical
and homeopathic.

During the initial diagnosis, there were injections and
creams and afternoons spent strapped into claustrophobic,
pulsating UV booths. When the more established medicines
and treatments began to fail and the purpled red scales and
clotted bruising upon my legs began to spread further, the doctors began to recommend alternative medicines: grainy min-
eral baths and kelp scrubs and a diet of oily fish and wonky,
purpled vegetables that looked like strange ruins. Liv had, of

course, been aware of all of this. She was a far better patient than me. She had attended every appointment and earnestly relished the opportunity to learn about new medications and sulphate-free shower washes. This sickish pink flesh mattered more to Liv than it did to me. She cared more about whether I ate the right fruit or vegetables or whether I applied daily cream and carried out booster cortisone shots each evening. Liv's diligence ensured I paid less attention. Rather than heeding the advice of my doctors, I instead persuaded myself that Liv would learn to love the abject blemishes that covered my body. Sometimes, when sitting in a café or pub, the edges of my trousers would rise slightly, exposing my ankles. People in pub gardens would direct their eyes towards me and then quickly, when I returned their stare, flash their gaze elsewhere. I knew that Liv would need to find a way of running her hand across a calf bruised with red scales and learn to find it tolerable. Liv approached all activities with a studious sense of intrigue so I simply placed great faith in knowing that she could replace disgust with misguided curiosity.

On the day of the healing, Liv had warned me that the initial walk would be steep. This long hike across swollen ground, a walk that was promised to be not much longer than forty minutes but was in fact almost a sheer climb, seemed like a punishment for my decision to wear new trainers. They were already pulling tightly across my Achilles heel and I knew that soon a rounded blister would sit right underneath the strap. Liv had never liked people who wore trainers. She had made disparaging comments about how everyone in London wore the same ones. It was customary for Liv to make these sorts of indiscriminate sweeping generalisations with unsettling conviction but without much recourse to conclusive explanation. These small, previously unremarkable differences of taste and character had begun to materialise as problematic in the most mundane of activities. A difference in footwear, or an alternative method for frying eggs or cooking spaghetti had become a painful way for Liv to extirpate common ground that had once been held as sacred.

We had picked up food for a picnic at Budgens. Each choice

I made became more impossible as I pictured Liv sat in her car picking a route across a map. I perused the aisles methodically but quickly, looking to shelves and back to the basket again with growing uneasiness. At the very beginning, I used to think Liv might find my confidence when grocery shopping an appealing quality, that if I made the right decision about bread, it would miraculously reveal my desirability. Years later, I was no longer satisfied that my food choices could make things so straightforward. I slid my phone out of my pocket, debating whether I should call Liv in the car to ask for her opinion. Deciding against it, I returned my phone, but continued to stroke it like a pebble as I brushed past shelves of organic vegetables and local, home-grown produce, quickly swapping leafy clementines for satsumas and dusty brown mackerel for blush salmon. The article had provided no instructions as to what might be best for the ceremonial healing.

As I returned to the car, I carefully stored our picnic in the boot where dry mud caked the floor. Before we pulled away, there had been a flapping of ordnance survey maps as we traced our fingers across small blue lines, looking for small triangles and cragged shapes of soft blue. Despite attempts at learning on numerous occasions, I had never really known how to read a map, but Liv scanned the crosshatched colours and uttered local place names and compass points with garrulous assurance. Liv projected the kind of unflappable confidence that ensured she appeared excellent at almost everything she turned her attention to. I trusted everything she said as true but envied the unshakeable faith with which she offered it.

I had misjudged the map and we had driven past the spot where we needed to park, so we came back on ourselves and righted the route. I packed the food and water in my bag and quickly slicked sun cream across my face despite the cool spring air. We pulled cream lambswool jumpers over our heads and Liv swapped brown suede lace ups for walking boots. The ascent was indeed steep and I forced myself to concentrate on the patter of my feet, trying to find a rhythm that ensured my rising breath was inaudible. We walked further and further and peeled off layers of clothing, tucking them into the crevices of our backpacks awkwardly. Liv picked up a stick every now and again and used it to stride forward, pacing steadily ahead of me. Every now and again she looked back at me offering particulars and idiosyncrasies about the landscape like a gift.

As we marched on, the dark green pool of water spread out in front of us. It was quiet but the creak of the air brushing through the lavender tussocks could be heard like a murmur. Heather sat at the water's edges and two mountains met in the middle, producing a cleft in the sky: a deep blue vase filled with wisps of cloud. I strode towards the edge, kneeling and dipping my fingers in; the silver of the ring on my index finger disfigured beneath the water.

Shall we eat or swim first? Liv asked, as if to placate the growing sense of apprehension that had gathered as we walked. I quickly remembered that we hadn't packed towels, which seemed only foolish considering we had come here to swim. *Do you think we should swim if we don't have towels?* I replied. Liv returned my gaze with quiet frustration, but then assured me that it was fine, that if anything it might be better that I dry naturally, and began pulling her jeans past her knees. Approaching the water, her left arm protruding slightly to steady her entry, she did not flinch and without looking at me called me towards her, telling me the water was refreshing, holding out her expectant palm.

I hesitated momentarily. Before the red, scaly skin condition had really settled in, there was great delight in the sweet slow pleasure of revelation, of pulling off t-shirts, of wavering with playful intent as I finally unclasped my bra. I was never humiliated in being naked. But over time, and as the patches had spread across my arms and legs, the shame of exposure had hypostatised. Inside and in semi-darkness it was easier to undress. The shuffling of bed sheets distracted from the blotchy red patches that covered my arms and scalp and lower legs. I worked hard to keep covered, to angle my body with the movement of other bodies that showed the parts I wanted to be visible. I knew that my arms looked serene atop
40

a terracotta duvet: the smatter of freckles complementing the colours. If I could just keep below the sheets, mysteriously sheltered by Egyptian cotton, mastering an intimate choreography of show and tell with carefully placed material, we could still take pleasure in furtive breathing and hidden body parts.

In the cold, spring wind of the mountains I was reluctant to remove even my hat. The outside could magnify the naked vulnerability of disclosure; there was no teasing shadow play to hide behind. I stood up from the grass and faced the water. It didn't look like it could contain the healing qualities the paper had advertised. Liv had begun swimming lengths, her head bobbing in and out of the water gracefully. The blue surface unfolded in front of me like a table, almost perfectly symmetrical. This well-designed plaything seemed like it should be left untouched. I didn't want to be responsible for ruining the water on account of immersing myself in it for the supposed purpose of good health. Nonetheless, Liv continued to beckon me forward magnanimously. She had an uncanny way of persuading me to try things I didn't want to. I dipped my toe into the water, which suddenly looked thicker, and propelled myself into the pool in a clumsy half-dive, half-plank.

Under the water, I felt Liv's hands scoop me towards her, pulling me close so that I lay across her, like the article said, *like a baptism*. The sun bore down on us and the cold water ached across our skin. I could feel her eyes scanning my legs and stomach, as if she might expect the condition to disappear instantly. *Imagine if you could swim in this water every day,* Liv whispered excitedly. I could have given her every ounce of my flesh. *Your skin would clear up in no time at all,* she continued with a tone that was clearly designed to reassure but implicitly signified her need for my return to good health. As Liv held me, I began to consider what I would need to do to swim in this little fresh tarn every single day. I wondered about the bloody-minded practicality of it all – the unfaltering dedication – and decided not to tell Liv that she was too idealistic for her own good.

As if sensing my burgeoning irascibility, Liv informed me that the instructions demanded I remain in the water for at least twenty minutes. She announced that she wanted to eat, removed her hands and pulled herself from the water. As she removed her grip, a very singular sense of tragedy overwhelmed me: a sadness that my body had simply been left to drift through the water unaided. I propelled my legs downwards and swam further out into the water defiantly. I thought about the article, how I needed to maximise my exposure to the bicarbonate and sulphate, somewhere in the aphotic layers of the water. I pushed myself further, amphibious, water and seaweed rippling through my fingers as I swam towards the centre of the pool. In the very middle, I let my feet find the swampy floor and forced myself so violently under the surface that I felt a surge of shock as my eyes opened to the murky olive underworld.

As I climbed out, Liv segmented the satsumas I had bought for lunch. She tore a chunk of bread and placed a grape in her mouth triumphantly. I lay on the ground like a dried out stone. Skin peeled off my legs, searing with the cold. We sat in the penumbra of the afternoon light and Liv untangled a smooth piece of seaweed that was twisted around my ankle, softly stroking the smooth scales down my left leg. Stopping suddenly, she held her hand in front of her; red scales and white powder caked her hand. The sky had begun to turn a cool grey. I looked into her eyes and knew that I would have dived even deeper. *Let's hope that article was right,* she smiled.

***

One night, a year or so after the healing, I find myself throwing my pillow from side to side. I allow my body to move with the demands of discomfort that a simple activity like going to bed can bring. I whack my head against the pillow because I can feel the contours of the soft foamy insides bunching against my scalp. It is hot even in the winter. I shrug the covers off, kicking them with dragging force from below. There is another body there in the dark. She reaches down and pulls the covers up towards her, coating us again. We have only really begun to learn how to share our bed, but she is soft and gracious, as she is in all things. I reach out for her hand, a finger to clasp – an arm that I love in stillness as much as I do in wild gesticulation. I remember that I have dreamt that I watch from afar as every room in her house, one by one, fills with fire. It is not the sort that consumes but instead seems to slowly fill the room like thick paint.

As I wake up, I peel off my pyjamas and find flakes of dust, snowy powder, covering the sheets. I scratch and pull at my pyjamas, yanking them up past my calves and knees to find myself scratching deeply into my skin, so that blood begins to pool once more and I find more white powder under my nails. Small spots of blood cover the sheets around my legs. If I were a murder victim in a detective series and suddenly one day found dead, the forensic scientists performing the autopsy would only find congealed steroid cream and my own dead skin cells beneath my nails.

I roll over to find that Hannah is looking at me. I realise that she has been stroking the small dimple of my shoulder for a little while now. Inside her room, I am perfectly imperceptible. She moves out of bed, folding the white duvet back in on itself. I watch as she catches herself in the mirror. It is a relief as she looks back at me as she walks towards the door. After she has returned from the bathroom, she slides back down under the sheets, carrying with her a rippling outside air that doesn't belong to this room just yet. In the bathroom, I cup cold water in my hands and splash it across my legs. The liquid prickles and I breathe slowly, allowing the water to dampen my feet. I return to Hannah's bedroom and she busies herself at the other side of the room, looking back at me every now and again, gesturing quietly and sweetly as the morning light eats the room.

44

An Exceptional Pain
Stephanie Boland
[Content note: blood]

When the pain starts, it is like a headache, only lower. The unfamiliarity of it makes me gasp; the strangeness of a pain normally felt in one place located in another. Eventually, I will discover a book called *A Headache in the Pelvis*, and realise this sort of pain is actually extremely common. But that is yet to come: it is months before its daily recurrence will become inevitable, its presence something which makes me sigh at every email and fume when the person in front of me at the ticket barriers takes a long time to find their Oyster card. On the first day, there is only this new pain – and, an hour later, a bright rose smear on the toilet tissue.

By the next spring the pain is not quite constant but it is grinding, debilitating, turning my brain to fog, making me irritable and terse with colleagues, friends, my partner. And although I feel people would understand me better if they knew what was going on, I don't want to tell people about my pain. It feels humiliating to admit that, at any given time, there is a (say) one-in-three chance that I'm in pain, a humiliation made worse by the fact that the pain seems to relate somehow to my reproductive system. Simultaneously, I feel that I might be 'cheating' to say something: after all, I can still write an email or an essay. (As I write this, it strikes me as an almost ludicrously gendered response. Even though I am in pain as I write this.) Most often, I say nothing. At the same time, I wonder if people would find my increasingly spiky personality more bearable if they knew why I always seem, at best, a few wrong sentences from anger, why I now sometimes take a long time to recall names, or dates, or what I came in to the kitchen for. If they knew I do not want to be touched because the space between my ribcage and thighs has become, essentially, dead ground, entirely unknown to me.

Because I am not speaking about the pain, I read about it. Sally Rooney's *Conversations with Friends* is good ('one of the best representations of endometriosis in fiction', my

45

friend says when she recommends it to me, and I suspect she is right). In *The Year of Magical Thinking*, Joan Didion – writing about her late husband and less than a year later, in *Blue Nights* about her late daughter – is better. Hilary Mantel is best. Follow the Mantel pain syllabus and one has an LRB diary, several books and countless interviews to study, all about the mind-calcifying experience of long-term sickness. As I double up queasily on bus after bus, she becomes my guide – her exploration of illness a roadmap towards understanding what it might mean to live with my own, lesser pain.

***

Here is what medical studies tells us about pain: That experts believe that women are faster to seek help for pain, faster to recover from it, and less likely to let pain control their lives. That despite this, doctors are more likely to underestimate the extent of women's pain and more likely to believe that they are engaging in exaggeration, hysteria or worry. That 70 per cent of the people impacted by chronic pain have "female" bodies (that is to say, assigned female at birth: cis women, trans men and non-binary people), but 80 per cent of studies are conducted on bodies the researchers categorise as "male" (mice or human). That the category of people socialised as "women" are less likely to be heard by their doctors; that any bodies other than cis male are ones are less likely to be seen. That the scenario I am about to recount as a white cis woman is still one of the better ones; that these figures are even worse for women of colour; that trans women's bodies are considered even more of a problem.

Here is what medical studies do not tell us: that to live with chronic pain is to live in a different world. That the afternoons are longer here, early evenings, too, the period between 5 and 7am the longest of all. That, when it comes to it, feels surprisingly normal to spend a year living in a trance, effectively controlled by a sharp throb in the guts. That chronic pain has a biblical quality to it, conjuring up ancient guilt, old sorrow, bone-deep exhaustion. That the sufferer may find

46

herself doing strange things, refusing food, or adding Genesis 3:16[1] to her stack of illness reading (is it or is it not my fault?) That it is very easy to begin hurting her body: to leave hot water bottles against her stomach until the skin mottles and burns; to drive a fist as deep as possible into the flesh, creating a different sort of ache, one that can at least be controlled. That to encounter her animal nature is always to encounter mortality. That she can feel both trapped by a body and a million miles away from it all at once; can feel that it is surely not hers; that she must have been handed the wrong form to inhabit, and that there ought to be a way to break through her chest and claw her way out, leaving it behind like a shed skin, a grisly discarded suit.

'In sickness,' Mantel writes, 'we can't avoid knowing about our body and what it does, its animal aspect, its demands.'[2] What she does not say, at least explicitly, is how profoundly alienating it is to encounter this animal self. It is not only that pain draws awareness to the body, to the fact that we are, essentially, made of meat; able to imagine that we feel ourselves bruising and marbling deep in the guts. At our worst, we are limited to our animal responses: from the jump of a stubbed toe to the howl of childbirth. Sometimes, the pain is so bad that, if I am alone, I will whimper like a wounded dog. After these episodes, there is blood.

***

In her memoir *In Gratitude*, written when she had terminal cancer, Jenny Diski recounts how she is upset and frustrated when the steroids she has been prescribed cause her to 'balloon up'. The fat, she writes, 'feels as if my body has been stuffed with some alien gel settled in particular places'.[3]

1   "I will make your pains in childbearing very severe;
with painful labor you will give birth to children."
Holy Bible, New International Version, 3:16
2   Hilary Mantel, '*Diary*', (London: London Review of Books, 2010), Vol 32, No 2, pp.41-2
3   Jenny Diski, *In Gratitude* (London: Bloomsbury, 2016).

In her introduction, Anne Enright notes that Diski could 'be a bit funny'[4] about people gaining weight. But reading her account of gaining it, shot through with such evident anguish, I wonder if Diski's issue with is as much to do with the disquieting experience of having one's body change of its own accord as it is to do with the realisation that she is no longer the slim woman of her wellness. 'For much of her life Mantel has felt she is inhabiting a stranger's body,'[5] says Sophie Elmhirst in her 2012 profile of the writer who famously self-diagnosed her own endometriosis aged twenty-seven. My pain, too, has become a matter of jurisdiction. When my partner absent-mindedly hugs me in bed, I have to move his hand from the stomach which no longer feels like mine.

***

In his *Atlantic* essay 'How Doctors Take Women's Pain Less Seriously', Joe Fassler writes that his wife Rachel's diagnosis of kidney stones after being admitted to hospital was 'a denial of the specifically female nature'[6] of the searing abdominal pain which later turned out to be an ovarian torsion. Writing in the *New York Times' Sunday Review* in 2013, Laurie Edwards quotes 'the oft-cited study', 'The Girl Who Cried Pain: A Bias Against Women in the Treatment of Pain', which found that women were more likely 'to have their pain characterised as "emotional," "psychogenic" and therefore "not real".'[7]

On the phone to 111 I experience the opposite: 'You have

4   Anne Enright, 'Introduction', *In Gratitude* by Jenny Diski (London: Bloomsbury, 2016)

5   Sophie Elmhirst, 'The Unquiet Mind of Hilary Mantel', (*New Statesman*, 2012) <www.newstatesman.com/node/147951>

6   Joe Fassler, 'How Doctors Take Women's Pain Less Seriously', (*The Atlantic*, 2015) <www.theatlantic.com/health/archive/2015/10/emergency-room-wait-times-sexism/410515/>

7   Laurie Edwards, 'The Gender Gap in Pain', (*New York Times' Sunday Review,* 2014) <www.nytimes.com/2013/03/17/opinion/sunday/women-and-the-treatment-of-pain.html>

an IUD,' the nurse on the phone explains to me patiently, 'so of course you're in pain. It's just settling down. This is very normal. Have you taken some ibuprofen?'

'Yes, buckets of it, always,' I want to say, 'and it barely touches it.' I want to say: 'I sit at my work desk every day, taking doses back-to-back.' I want to say: 'I am fairly sure my liver will give in before I figure out why I am in pain.' Yet I know it would be hopeless. In this and every subsequent encounter with a doctor, there is a sense, almost ecclesiastic, that this is an ordinary part of the female experience, or at least the sexualised female experience. This is the real-life reality that the snake in the garden story is designed to explain: You are an adult female, ergo there will be pain. There's a piece of metal inside your reproductive system, so of course it hurts. If you went with another contraceptive method, there'd be vomiting or anger or bloating. On balance, we recommend the piece of metal. ('Coils pain you, jellies are damp,' Dorothy Parker did not write but could have, although these cramps are like none I have ever known.)

'Assigning a value to my own pain has never ceased to feel like a political act,' explains Eula Biss. But this cuts both ways: 'I struggle to consider my pain in proportion to the pain of a napalmed Vietnamese girl whose skin is slowly melting off as she walks naked in the sun. This exercise itself is painful.' [8]

I imagine my pain against that of a friend-of-a-friend who has had his life, in his mid-twenties, turned upside down by illness; against the friend who already knows she cannot have children; against, indeed, childbirth. Next to these, my pain is nothing. I could keep going and going forever with it (well, until I stop). But should I have to? Does the pain not signal something is wrong? Does it matter if it does? How long into this process will I pretend to be cool? Until they cut me open and take some part of me away? Until I can't work? In *The Year of Magical Thinking*, after Didion arrives at the hospital and learns her husband has died, she hears one of the

8   Eula Biss, 'The Pain Scale', (Readings in *Harper's Magazine*, 2005), p.12.

medical professionals call her a 'cool customer'[9] – a persona she adopts ambivalently, as she manages, in both senses, the fallout from her husband's death. What, she wonders, would someone who is not a 'cool customer' be permitted to do?

***

One day, I am walking to work in Westminster in so much pain that my legs begin to shake and my eyes tear up as I cross the bridge and head towards Parliament Square. There are already tourists out in the watery first light: a Chinese woman in a wedding dress stands in front of the palace, surrounded by photographers. Nobody has noticed me. I feel like I will pass out, or vomit. I pass a group of policemen outside Parliament and wonder briefly what would happen if I just sank down beside them on the concrete, put my back to the wall and refused to move, weak and pale and gently sweating. Would they pick me up? Send me home?

I picture all the other women walking around London feeling like they might faint or vomit or both. What does it mean for the collective female psyche to have one in six of us living with invisible pain?

'I have been so mauled by medical procedures, so sabotaged and made over, so thin and so fat, that sometimes I feel that each morning it is necessary to write myself into being,' Mantel says.

Writing to you now, I feel as if I am sending some secret note from beyond the veil, from the world where the mysteriously pained live.

I go into work.

***

At home, my partner fills another hot water bottle. I am lying on our sofa, breathing deep into the cavity below my navel. 'I'm so sorry,' I say. 'I'm so bored of this. You must

9   Joan Didion, *The Year of Magical Thinking*, (London, New York, Toronto and Sydney: Harper Perennial, 2009), p. 15

be, too.'

'Steph,' he says, 'come on.'

I listen to him in the kitchen, putting on the kettle, and remember my Jungian friend explaining that sometimes it is kindness, not cruelty, that is the biggest threat to our sense of self. I am scared my partner will get tired of my pain, which has begun to recur so often in our conversations (although still not as often as it occurs in my body).

When he seems not to – when he continues to be kind and worried and treats me with more and more love, bringing me countless hot water bottles and quietly taking on more of the housework – it is almost unbearable.

***

'Move your leg just a little wider there,' the nurse says, as she manipulates the probe to look at my right and then left ovary. Her body is warm and soft holding me in place, and I have a sudden urge to stress to her just how much it hurts and how often; to tell her that I've tracked it with an app and that there was only three days last month where I wasn't in pain, and would that change her ideas about what this might be? Does it change what she's seeing at all? I realise I need, desperately, for her to care about me.

Only it turns out she's not seeing anything: 'The IUD looks fine,' she tells me. 'And I can't see any fibroids or cysts.'

I keep looking at the tiles on the ceiling, letting her finish. The results will be with my doctor in a week's time. Yes, I'll have to ring them, she doesn't think they'll call.

I'm reminded of all the women I've seen in films and on television, also staring up at doctors' ceilings. When I try to look one up on YouTube after – gynaecology exam episode girls – all that comes up is porn. 'Girl gets excited during her gynaecology exam!' That'd be the day. After a bit of Googling, I try again with the name of the episode and watch '*Girls*, Vagina Panic end'. The main character, Hannah, is having a routine exam with an older woman doctor when she begins rambling insensitively and nonsensically about HIV.

51

'If you have AIDS there's a lot of stuff people won't ask you about: no-one's going to call you up and say, did you get a job, did you pay your rent, did you take an HTML course, all they're going to say is congratulations on not being dead.' Her doctor rebukes her – 'that is an incredibly silly thing to say. You do not want AIDS' but she misses the point. 'You could not pay me enough to be twenty-four again,' the doctor says. 'Well, they're not paying me at all,' says Hannah, before looking up at the ceiling and wincing. 'Is that painful?' 'Yes,' says Hannah: 'but only in the way it's supposed to be.'

Watching this scene now, after my appointment, I am torn. On the one hand, Hannah's character is so tone-deaf that I watch through my hands. On the other, there is, I can't deny, something in this idea of the pain that we are supposed to feel versus that we are not supposed to feel. What Hannah seeks – in her idiotic way – is an exceptional pain: something which the world will be forced to acknowledge; which she will not be expected to put up with.

When I leave the hospital after my scan, I stand confused at the entrance, unsure what to do now. I feel like I might cry; I almost want to cry. I certainly want a passerby to ask me if I'm all right. But nobody does – of course; it's mid-afternoon in London – and so I walk up the street to catch the bus home, quiet, anonymous, the pain just starting its slow fade in the vicinity of that tricky-to-see left ovary.

***

One day, there is no pain, and it is as if every other day the world had been sepia-toned until now, only I had not noticed. With the thin gauze of pain removed, the colours were restored to the trees and the red to the London busses. Suddenly, I can remember a time when every day was like this, comfortable and bright, my body moving easily through the world, walking the miles from Whitechapel to Euston in one go, or standing up on the tube all the way to work without a thought, without a cold sweat and laboured breath. These painless hours feel like visiting a city I lived in long ago: a different world, inhabited by a different person. The birds, I realise, are singing outside my bedroom window. My mind feels light and clear.

'Pain,' says Mantel, 'is a present tense business.'

Biss says that after a year of pain, she realised she could no longer remember what she felt like to not be in pain.

The occasional lulls make the pain, when it returns, so much worse.

***

'Maybe I'm dying,' I joke, with a mean hopelessness, to my boyfriend. On another day, in a more serious mood, I ask: 'which would be worse: if I was diagnosed with something fatal, or if this was just it, and I'm in pain forever?' 'Come on,' he says. 'You know which would be worse.' Well, yes. I am becoming as unlikeable as Hannah Horvath. But I know how to be stoic in the face of diagnosable pain and illness. I don't know how to behave with this endless discomfort. I recall the number of people who are seriously ill for years before they're given a diagnosis. It occurs to me that I am probably taking this too seriously, or else not nearly seriously enough. The novelist Sarah Perry, writing about her diagnosis of Graves disease in the *Guardian*, describes being 'taken over by a great sense of shame . . . ashamed of my despondency, of my bad temper, ashamed to so bitterly resent my expulsion from the Vale of Health.'[10]

Biss writes that she is 'comforted, oddly, by the possibility that you cannot compare my pain to yours [and] cannot prove it insignificant.' I, in turn, am comforted by Biss writing this, even as I try to remember to count my blessings.

***

It's 9am on a weekday, and I'm at the health centre instead

10   Sarah Perry, "I was weak, despairing, confused': did writing a novel make me ill?', (*Guardian*, 2017), <www.theguardian.com/lifeandstyle/2017/jan/28/did-writing-a-book-make-me-ill-graves-disease-sarah-perry>

of work. My new doctor thinks I have bowel trouble.

But the blood follows the pain exactly, I tell him. To the hour. And the pain follows the menstrual cycle.

'Women' Laurie Edwards says, 'are more likely to receive diagnoses of "nebulous" conditions – like fibromyalgia or chronic fatigue syndrome – which 'illustrate[s] the problems associated with the reliability of the female patient as narrator of her pain.[11] (Here, Edwards conflates "woman" with "female", by which she presumably means those assigned female at birth.)

'The only thing we could do,' my new doctor says, 'is send you for another test. Then they'd probably remove your IUD, which we don't want. And we avoid the test on women who are pre-partum. You don't have children, do you?'

His look feels like a challenge. 'No,' I say.

'Well, it comes with a risk, so we don't do it for childless women.'

Well, I want to say, I'm not going to have a baby anyway if I'm in horrific pain half the time, am I?

(For twenty-five years I knew I did not want children; counted it a fact as sure as my own name, or as breathing. What if the decision is no longer mine?)

Instead, I say: 'So what happens next?'

I have checked every box: I am a white, confident, cisgender, have no visible disabilities, am a middle-class woman. I'm well-spoken and polite but insistent. I'm a cool customer (read: not hysterical) but one who knows how to advocate for herself (read: not a pushover), and I've told the doctor three times that the pain is not indigestion (read: willing to compensate for his profession's tendency to not listen to women). After this appointment, I will go back to my good job, where people value my expertise and listen to my ideas. I am serious and young and I have brought every privilege in here with me, earned and not, hard-won and unfairly incidental, and still the male doctor can say – does say: no, sorry, the possibility

11   Laurie Edwards, 'The Gender Gap in Pain', (*New York Times'* *Sunday Review*, 2014) <www.nytimes.com/2013/03/17/opinion/sunday/women-and-the-treatment-of-pain.html>

of some future children at some imagined future time must come first. That's just how we do it. That's just how it is.

Even though it is a bright, cold, sunny day, this time, I do cry. I cry outside the surgery, standing confused and lost as a child – just like I did in front of the hospital a few weeks before – and I cry on the top deck of the bus back to the office, hopeless and frustrated and angry at this body I've been forced to live inside.

After I have stopped crying, a man gets on wearing a King's College University ID around his neck, and a short while later I realise he's checking me out.

***

Early one morning, in the strange twilight before dawn, the word 'pain' throbs in my thoughts. A woman's pain is never done, I recite in my head, and when it's done, it's under-pained. This amuses me. What might under-pained mean? An injury that is under-articulated; under-felt, even? One that a woman is not at pains to express? Being 'at pains' is, after all, to do with the seriousness of one's want, with its integrity. It invokes a moment when our desire is so serious that it touches the physical. (Honesty, too, is often prefaced with the word 'painful'.)

In Descartes' *Meditations*, Cartesianism is explained by comparing the mind-body relationship negatively with that of a pilot in a ship. 'I am not only lodged in my body,' Descartes says, 'but ... joined to it very closely and indeed so compounded and intermingled with my body, that I form, as it were, a single whole with it.' Our bodies are not vessels which we steer; they are part of us. We cannot so much as think without them.

Compare that with Mantel on Henry VIII: 'His leg caused him chronic pain and historians – and, I'm afraid, doctors – underestimate what chronic pain can do to sour the temper and wear away both the personality and the intellect.'[12]

12   Hilary Mantel, 'Royal Bodies', (4th Estate Blog, 2013) <www.4thestate.co.uk/2013/02/royal-bodies-hilary-mantel/>

It occurs to me that trying to articulate the meaning of a term invented idly in bed at 5am is perhaps not worthwhile.

***

One night, I come home late, when my partner is already in bed, and – tiptoeing around the flat – find a letter for me. It's from the NHS, and it tells me that I have, after all, been booked in for the next scan, on 14 February. Valentine's day.

'Maybe two men will touch me that day!' I joke to my boyfriend, who is kind enough to laugh. He has already told me that if they have to remove the IUD we will find something else, has already raged against the long waiting times and patronising doctors, has already given me a thousand small acts of love as I grouse and grimace and gasp. What, after all, is one more?

It is frustrating that I did not know this letter was coming. It has taken a long time to arrive.

But somewhere, there is a woman on the bus, who does not think about her body at all, but only the watery sunlight and journey into town. Sometimes, I can almost be her. Until then, I survive; unexceptionally pained.

The Sex Game
Rachel Heng

When Lily was ten and Zoey was eight, they used to play the sex game. The game was simple. There was the sex bed, and there was the giving birth bed. First you had sex with a bolster on the sex bed, then gave birth to a pillow on the giving birth bed. The idea was, after giving birth they went straight back to having sex, but Zoey kept adding a stage: the baby bed. She would stop at the baby bed, nursing her newborn with imaginary milk bottles (because breastfeeding was weird). This frustrated Lily. She explained again and again that wasn't the point of the game. There was no baby bed. The baby bed was from a game they used to play a long time ago, when they were kids, and now they were no longer kids and the sex game was a totally different game altogether. Didn't Zoey get it?

Lily spent weekends at Zoey's house, because Zoey's house had a piano she could practise on. Their own piano had been sold, together with a lot of other stuff, like her mother's Chanel handbag that she knew cost more than two-thousand dollars and the sparkly diamond earrings Lily had been given for her eighth birthday. Her mother had cried when they took Lily's things to the pawnshop, but Lily didn't mind. She did not care for the sparkly earrings and uncomfortable shoes that she was made to wear on festive occasions.

The idea was, this way Lily could keep up with the piano, even though they now all lived squished together in her grandmother's two-bedroom flat. The piano lessons seemed to mean something to Lily's mother. She would sell her handbags and her jewellery, she would take a job as a receptionist after twenty years of being a housewife, she would sleep with her two children in a single cramped room that smelled of herbal ointments, but she would not give up Lily's piano lessons. That was how it was decided that Lily would stay with Zoey every weekend.

Zoey lived in a condominium with rolling manicured lawns and an Olympic-sized swimming pool. It was very nice, but it was still a step down from the semi-detached house that Lily's family had lived in. The hierarchy of real estate went: detached, semi-detached, terrace house, condominium, HDB flat. Every Singaporean child learnt this around the same time they started going to school. It was the same with parents' professions. Zoey's father worked in an oil company and made a lot of money, but Lily's father was a lawyer. And everyone knew that with jobs it went: doctor, lawyer, architect, engineer. So Zoey always accorded Lily the due respect. After all, the situation with her grandmother's flat was only temporary.

Zoey listened seriously when Lily told her there was no baby bed. She tried her best to understand. She knew what sex was, that wasn't the problem. Her parents believed in fostering a learning culture at home, so she had been given books with comic strips in them that explained it all. She had questions, of course, like how a boy's thing would fit into a girl's while lying down, when all the drawings showed it to be perpendicular? They talked about these questions over the phone sometimes, when Lily called her during the week. 'Zoey,' she'd say, 'it's me, Lily.' And Zoey would always know to take the cordless phone away into her room, shutting the door behind her, before they started talking.

***

When Lily was twelve and Zoey was ten, Zoey's parents threw her a birthday party by the Olympic-size swimming pool. Lily's mother made her go, even though everyone there would be younger than her and therefore not very fun. Lily's mother was invited too.

At the party, Zoey's father grilled chicken wings and Taiwanese sausages with a serious frown on his face. He was quite muscular for a father and Zoey's mother touched his waist a lot. Zoey's mother wore her hair short like a boy and had very tanned skin. In her wide-brimmed hat and big sunglasses, she looked like a movie star. She always made sure to cut the black bits off the chicken wings before giving them to
58

her daughter, because they caused all kinds of horrible diseases, such as cancer.

Lily was the only one there in a two-piece swimsuit. All the other girls wore Speedo and Arena one-pieces, as if they were there for a swim meet. Lily's had strings that tied at the neck and back, and inserts that made it look like she had a figure. Red and orange flowers bloomed across her chest and bottom. Her mother had the same bikini in blue – they had bought them together from a dusty street-side stall while on holiday in Bintan. Her mother was not wearing a hat or sunglasses; she wasn't even wearing a swimsuit because she had come straight from the clinic. She still wore her blue and white receptionist uniform and a little scarf tied around her neck, which Lily usually found very trim and pretty. The other mothers were not all trim, many were soft and liver-spotted, with low, elongated breasts and solid middles. None of them wore uniforms.

The only boys there were younger brothers who clung to their parents, so the girls were free to shout and run without inhibitions. Soon they were doing somersaults off diving boards, swimming like sharks and bombing down the children's slides, shrieking hysterically. The sun was all around them, bouncing and jetting off the droplets that sprayed through the humid air, at once fierce and lazy in the way that only a tropical midday could be. When the girls finally lifted themselves out of the water, poolside concrete marking red dots on tender forearms, their noses were flushed and their hair stringy. They collapsed in the shade, fanning themselves with paper plates and sipping fruit punch watered down with rapidly melting ice.

Lily was having fun. The smell of chlorine and sizzling meat was full of promise, lulling her into the feeling that life would always be like this. That there would always be cold, clear water to plunge into on a sweaty day and that a plate of perfectly barbecued wings would always be waiting when one emerged hungry from the water, tired and wrung out in the way that only trying to stay afloat could make you.

The girls were busy admiring Zoey's house. They all loved

59

it, loved the big, clean swimming pool with its wooden decking and resort-style umbrellas; the fast, silent lifts that took you to the top floor; Zoey's room filled with colourful Ikea furniture, books and the twinkling blue heart-shaped nightlight.

They talked about other houses they liked. One of the girls' families had just moved into a new condominium by the beach. It had a pool that looked as if it led straight into the open sea. The girl informed them that they were called infinity pools. Everyone wanted an infinity pool when they grew up and got their own houses. Another girl's parents had just converted the guest bedroom into a TV room, with a huge flat screen that took up half the wall, a mini fridge and beanbag chairs. Everyone also wanted beanbag chairs in their houses.

Then Zoey, always conscious of her friend, turned to Lily. Lily, she told the other girls proudly, lived in a semi-detached house. But it was huge for a semi-d, and was practically a bungalow. Lily's house had its own front garden and back garden, where there were bushes of little red flowers with nectar that you could eat. It had floor-to-ceiling sliding doors and a patio with a real picnic table, on which Lily's father served chocolate-chip pancakes every weekend. And if they liked the furniture in Zoey's room then, well, they should really see Lily's. Everything in Lily's room was purple, because purple was her favourite colour. The girls nodded approvingly. Lily had even been allowed to paint one wall bright purple, and how many parents were OK with that? Not many, the girls agreed. Clarissa's bedroom was yellow, but it was so pale it might as well have been white.

'Wow,' one of the girls said. 'What does your dad do? You must be really rich.'

'He's a corporate lawyer,' Lily answered automatically, scratching her thigh. The skin was red and tender from sunburn; she liked how it hurt to touch it. She looked over at where her mother was sitting, in her neat receptionist's uniform with the crimson scarf around her neck. Unlike the women she was surrounded by, who slouched and stretched, Lily's mother sat with her back straight, a bright smile on her face. Lily thought she looked beautiful.

'Yes, we're very lucky,' she said modestly and smiled, trying not to think about her grandmother's flat with its stained
walls and herbal smell. The other girls nodded, Zoey too,
even though she had heard it all before. They did not know
what a corporate lawyer was but it sounded better than a
regular lawyer, which was already pretty good.

The thought that perhaps Zoey never liked her, and was
lashing out in a flattering fake girl way, crossed Lily's mind.
But when she met Zoey's shining, proud gaze, Lily saw that
it was worse. Zoey believed it all: that Lily's father was away
on a long business trip; that it was only a matter of time before they moved back into their big, beautiful house; that they
couldn't have a piano in her grandmother's flat because old
people didn't like the noise.

The other girls were charmed. They couldn't stop talking
about the purple bedroom and the patio, even going so far as
to convince themselves that maybe a semi-detached was actually pretty much the same as a detached house, if they were
the same size. Lily kept smiling brightly at the girls, sitting
up straighter, a little queen in her red and orange two-piece
swimsuit. The heat was unforgiving even in the shade by the
pool, and a delicate crown of perspiration soon beaded her
young forehead.

***

When Lily was fourteen and Zoey was twelve, Lily's
mother said she wouldn't be going to Zoey's house anymore.
Her aunt had generously offered to give them her old piano,
now that the last of her children were married and had pianos
of their own. Lily didn't mind. The bus ride to Zoey's house
was too long and gave her motion sickness. She had also
decided that Zoey wasn't really a friend, since they only saw
each other because of their parents. Friends were people at
school whom she ate with and called in the afternoon to talk
about other people at school, not children of your parents'
friends.

The piano arrived without its bench. Lily's aunt called to say that it had been broken in transit, and that she was so sorry but she thought having the piano without a bench was at least better than nothing. Lily didn't mind. She practised while sitting on a dining chair that was too high, which made her neck ache and her elbows stiff, but it was better than nothing.

Lily didn't mind, but her mother seemed to. Now that Lily was fourteen, she noticed things. Things such as the mascara her mother had started wearing to work, and the Gillette Venus razor in the shower, a thick black hair curling around its triple-action smoothing blades. Her mother had never had hair on her legs. And now she noticed that when her mother told her she wouldn't be going to Zoey's house anymore, she smiled chirpily, in the way she only did when trying to convince Lily of something she didn't believe.

The doctor from Lily's mother's clinic started coming over to the flat. He usually came in the humid afternoons, when Lily had just got back from school, sweaty and tired. He sat on the couch swatting mosquitoes and speaking Hokkien with Lily's grandmother, who asked him questions like whether he had eaten yet and if he was working very hard given that he was a doctor. Lily was made to call him Uncle. Uncle never stayed very long. They would leave the flat together, Lily's mother telling her that she would be back in a while and to make sure her brother did his homework. When they left, Lily would clear away the mugs on the table, wiping it clean with a paper towel. Uncle never finished his coffee; always a quarter left, brown rings on the inside of the mug showing where he had paused before.

Lily's mother always came home in time for dinner. They never talked about Uncle. Lily's grandmother made them oily soups out of lotus roots, black chicken and bitter gourd, which they sipped in silence with their noses clenched tight. The soup left a dull, hostile aftertaste in the corners of their mouths. Lily's brother never drank them, and her mother never tried to make him. Lily drank them, just as Lily did her homework, came home straight after school and never talked
62

about Uncle.

***

When Lily was sixteen (and Zoey was fourteen), they moved out of her grandmother's flat. Their new home was still a flat, but it had a pedestal toilet and a kitchen floor without any missing tiles. The bathroom, if not completely modern, did not have moss growing under the sink or mould on the ceiling. For the first time in seven years, Lily's mother would have her own bedroom. Lily would still share with her brother, but they were to have beds instead of thin mattresses on the floor and desks for homework instead of the sticky kitchen table. The new flat was on the twelfth floor, which meant it was always filled with a delicious breeze when the windows were open. It did not smell like medicated ointments.

The days leading up to the move went by in a flurry of paint chips, fabric swatches and haggling with tattooed contractors in baggy vests. Lily and her mother drove to Malaysia for cheap furniture made of dark teak wood, Balinese resort style. Her brother tagged along, fake complaining about the shopping, but really pleased to be able to show off his strength by lifting heavy tables.

While searching for used bookcases, they found a piano bench in the dusty corner of a second-hand shop. It needed re-upholstering, but once that was done, it matched Lily's aunt's piano perfectly. For the first time since she had stopped going to Zoey's house, Lily could play without stopping to stretch every fifteen minutes.

Moving day arrived with the first of the monsoon rains. Lily woke up to lightning crackling across the sodden, Saturday sky, and fat raindrops sprinkling her feet through the open window. She counted to four before the thunder sounded. Her mother and brother were still asleep, she on her back with an arm drawn across her eyes, he on his side, curled like a snail without a shell. Lily looked around at the room that the family had lived in since her father left, at the wardrobe that didn't shut, the dressing table with its peeling, yellowing laminate and the marbled floor with its green and white flecks. These details, which in her mind had never quite stopped being temporary, now struck her as strangely comforting. She got up to close the window and then lay back down on the mattress, pretending to sleep until her mother woke up.

Relatives they usually only saw at Chinese New Year came to help with the move, oddly decked out in t-shirts and flip-flops. In Lily's mind they wore new dresses and carried oranges in little red paper bags all year round. On arrival, they shouted greetings at each other and made blunt comments about Lily's haircut. They gasped at the weight of boxes and tutted over the contents of the fridge. They had arguments about who would carry what with whom and in whose car. Lily's grandmother's tiny flat was filled to the brim with all of them, shouting and laughing and scolding.

They did not have many things to move. All the furniture was her grandmother's, so everything that they owned fit into several large boxes and suitcases. The only thing they really needed help with was the piano, which the relatives wrapped in plastic sheets to protect from the rain, squabbling over who would lift which corner. The move itself only took one trip in two cars and a van.

In the new flat, Lily's mother opened all the windows, even though it was still raining. The wind that whipped through the freshly painted rooms smelled of trees and wet cement, a familiar smell within unfamiliar walls.

Lily slipped away to her room as soon as she could, closing the door behind her. The room did not yet contain anything from the old flat, only the new beds, desks and side tables. She ran her toes over the wood laminate floors, fingered the thick, spotless curtains and bounced gently on the bed that was closer to the window. She decided that this bed would be hers, and the one against the wall, her brother's. Lying down, she saw that the ceiling was smooth and white, free of water stains.

With the door closed it was silent, and it was almost as if she were already an adult with a job, doing something creative and interesting like publishing or graphic design, who spent Saturday afternoons lying in bed because she had a busy evening involving cocktails and rooftop bars ahead of her. Yes, that was the kind of young woman who would live alone in a flat like this, with wood laminate floors and windows in every room. Lily lay like this until someone called her name, then she went outside and was polite.

When the relatives left, Lily helped her mother with the unpacking. Her job was to break down the boxes that were too large to be thrown down the rubbish chute. The corrugated cardboard resisted tearing, and Lily's hands were soon red from the effort. She enjoyed it, enjoyed folding the thick sheets until their skins tore, then ripping them slowly lengthwise, in the direction of the hidden pleats that gave them their strength. Letting the broken pieces fall about her in a pile, Lily was so absorbed that she didn't notice Uncle enter the living room.

Uncle sat down on the new couch, and Lily's mother disappeared into the kitchen. He had sat on their couch in her grandmother's flat all the time, but this was different. Here he leaned back a little more, spread his hairy, shirted arm across its spotless beige fabric and crossed his feet under the coffee table. It was only when he asked Lily how she liked the new flat that she realised she didn't like it, she didn't like it at all.

She smiled and nodded politely, said that it was very nice indeed, but try as she might, she couldn't bring herself to say what he wanted to hear: thank you. She looked down, kept tearing the cardboard into pieces, but the joy had gone out of it now. Lily's mother came back into the living room, carrying a cup of coffee.

***

When Lily was twenty-eight and Zoey was twenty-six, they both went to get pedicures at a trendy Orchard Road salon on a hot Sunday morning. Lily stood stiffly with her mother in the sleek white reception, filling out a registration form. 'Why do they need my marital status, profession and number of children to give me a pedicure?', Lily was asking her mother, when she saw Zoey's face in profile, laughing with the receptionist. Zoey didn't need to register because she was a regular at the salon. The receptionist called her Mrs Lim.

Zoey sat down next to them on the couch. The cream leather buckled prettily under her weight. She took out a phone and swiped at its screen with slender fingers tipped in a shade of tasteful coral. When her hand was not swiping, it rested firmly on the hard bulge of her lululemon-clad stomach, fingers bent at the knuckle, gently claw-like.

As Lily wrote 'Single', 'Lawyer', 'Zero' on the form, clipboard balanced against a bony knee, she imagined how the conversation would go. 'Zoey,' she'd say, 'it's me, Lily.' Zoey would squint at her, the effort of sifting through fourteen years' worth of classmates, acquaintances and service staff showing on her plump unlined face, before the image of a long-limbed girl in a red and orange two-piece swimsuit would finally surface. It was likely that she would recognise Lily's mother first since she had changed less, having already been wrinkled and tired in the time that Zoey had known her.

Zoey should recognise her mother, even if she didn't recognise Lily. This thought sparked a slow, withering anger. Maybe she was pretending not to see them on purpose, stung by awkwardness from the unofficial parting all those years ago. But as Lily watched Zoey out of the corner of her eye, her mother explaining the difference between a regular and a gel pedicure in the background, she became convinced that Zoey did not recognise them.

The urge to speak to her was overwhelming. But Lily was afraid that once she started, she wouldn't be able to stop. That the words 'Zoey, it's me, Lily' would unstop everything else, like the part-time job she'd taken up in secondary school so she wouldn't have to take an allowance from her mother; the nights she skipped sleep to stay at the top of her class; the three clubs she'd chaired and captained and founded not out of enjoyment but to pad out her scholarship applications; the scholarship, that had only brought relief of not failing rather than any happiness or pride; the isolating Ivy League

66

law school; the fake American accent which had interviewers gushing over how 'good her English was'; the shiny office in Manhattan with a river view; and the one-bedroom apartment she rented in the West Village with crown mouldings, a fireplace and real hardwood floors, that she returned to laden with binders and Chinese takeaway each night. The fact that none of this was all that bad, that she was conscious of how lucky she was to have had any opportunities at all, how very, very lucky to have grown up in a place where all you had to do if you wanted a better life was to work hard.

The yearly trips home, where she saw her mother get frailer, less beautiful, more alone, when she agreed to get pedicures even though she hated them with a passion, hated sitting still in an over air-conditioned room smelling like lemongrass flicking through crumpled glossy magazines full of smiling women while someone sawed away at her toenails. Because it was a real shame that someone so clever and accomplished didn't take better care of herself.

The salon attendant drew back a heavy curtain, revealing the back room where jet whirlpools could be heard massaging calloused feet and paper lanterns cast a warm, caressing glow. She called Zoey's new name: Mrs Lim.

Zoey stood up carefully, one hand on the small of her back and one on her stomach, a pose they had imitated many times as little girls with pillows stuffed under their t-shirts. That's not the point of the game, Lily wanted to say, don't you get it? But she didn't, and Zoey disappeared behind the curtain.

What Her Bones Said

S. Niroshini

I

It is the memory of the abruptness of her disappearance that is most startling, how quickly a person can disappear, how the outline of a life can vanish without a moment's notice. All traces of a body —that nuisance, that pleasure, which one continuously seeks to interrogate— can be subsumed into nothing but empty gossip and air that is filled with innuendo and rumour. It was at a party in the botanical gardens of Peradeniya that she would last be seen, drinking a glass of ginger beer in a tea-cup. Laughing as her white cotton dress stuck to her sweaty back and her diamond ring glistened in the eyes of disappointed suitors. *The Field Guide to the Common Trees and Shrubs of Sri Lanka* lists the different ways it is possible to describe the surface of a leaf: stellate, tomentose, coriaceous. In this world, even nature had become colonised by language. I can see the scene when reports of her engagement first reached her home. A blur of men and women stand in the fading light of the evening, clasping their elbows as the happy news lit their faces. They move towards her from one corner of the long veranda, the gold jewellery they wear reflects luminous off their skin whilst a fan circles above them in the heat with inexplicable languor. As she stepped onto that fateful train, later, they thought that she was surely destined now to exist in other, more beautiful, possibilities.

II

She had held secrets between sternum and vertebrae. Her body turned into an archive: she knew the location of lost keys, the name of the thief who operated at the flower market, the affair between Mr Dhanapalan and wistful Upeksha. The most vivid memories though, she used to say, related to her childhood. In particular, the rush of activity surrounding her paternal grandfather's house when she was a child. Merchants walked in and out with the gait of kings, vegetable vendors advertised their wares on the smooth red steps to the house and the rain... the rain never stopped falling. Colombo then was a place of mischief and indecipherable motives, located in a thumb-print shaped island off the southern coast of India. In the early 1980s, conflicts persisted between the Singhalese and minorities, mainly Tamils. She doesn't recall being particularly perturbed by that latter fact as a child, it was simply a part of life. Her existence at that time, she would venture to say, was in fact a rather carefree period, unaware of the real trauma that had beholden less fortunate citizens of the country. It was the sensory pleasure of food that her generation most frequently recalled, a physical delight akin to a warm hand on the belly. Fish buns and butter cakes at birthday parties, the memory of being drunk on coconut water after an early morning dance class.

III

Twenty years ago, her grandfather swam into the ocean and also vanished. It was believed he had worn a three-piece suit, a final nod to grandeur completed with a patterned silk pocket square. Only his gold ring, encrusted with the nine stones of the planets, was found precariously perched on the marina. When the news was announced by his son, her father, there was almost a sense of casual inevitability that this is how it would occur. When she ventured into his private room in Bambalapitiya that day, everything from the bedsheets to her own clothes had the quality of blueness and stillness, like a pond at dusk. It was here that she would first experience the physical sensation of loss. In her memory, she waited by the entrance to the house peeping through the gap in the gate, its circular shape reflecting her own bowl-cut hairstyle, waiting for her grandfather to come home. Someone, most likely her mother, had lifted her up by her armpits to gaze through the hole. In this scene, it is curiously the back of her head which she sees in her memory. She is in essence seeing herself from afar. Let me tell you something. The body knows to distance itself from the mind during moments of pain, of trauma. How we are all witnesses to the events of our families, how we store such memories in our body. Now she is gone and no one can say where. History repeating itself? A salacious story no doubt which I have now shared with you. Other such secrets, too, are kept enclosed under my thirteenth rib bone for eternity.

1 January 2018 – Dissociation, Almost
Ari Potter

[Content note: dissociation, suicidal ideation, drug use]

A new year. It is 11am, and I'm unsure of time, and space, and everything feels slightly unreal.

I have not, contrary to what you might think, been up all night, partying until my bones are worn ragged. By 11.59pm on 31 December 2017, I was dancing alone in my room, having done a French exit from a party where most of my best friends were. I was asleep before the Hootenanny was even over. I am rested, yet when I wake upon the first day of the new year everything is just not quite as it should be.

I pick up the part-finished bottle of champagne that looks cheap but tastes expensive next to my bed. I decide that it would be appropriate for me — or the character that is me, who has been placed in this scene — to drink the champagne. I notice that the red dress I had been wearing has been cast to one side. I channel the girl that was wearing that dress (me, last night) singing 'Dancing In The Dark' and I bring the champagne to my lips. It is warm. I am reminded that prawn cocktail was a dish invented in the 70s. I gulp. The champagne goes down.

I get up. I go for a walk. I eat a sausage sandwich (vegan, fake cheese, fake mayo, delicious, leaving me to wax lyrical about the fact that the deliciousness of meat is overamplified and conditioned). By 10am, after an ill-advised watching of S04E03 of *Black Mirror*, I have lost it completely. The shape of 'it all' is lost. It has become difficult to conceive of anything as real, and not merely a cardboard construct of habits. I am struck by the fragility of my skin, and by the fact that if I can cut through chicken with a table knife, I can cut through my own skin too. And I might try it, just to see the blood ooze out, that shocking red that I can barely comprehend as real.

It is as though a very subtle Instagram filter has been cast over my eyes, making everything at once more vivid but less like it is actually happening. A zero-care attitude has gripped me, hauntingly familiar to the one that took over on 5 September 2016, just before I disappeared. 'Dissociative psychosis' was the official description. I prefer: the plane where the absurdity of 'it all' becomes so acutely felt that our shared world doesn't exist anymore. Not for you, not today. The physical and social laws that are supposed to bind us here have dissolved. I am about to say goodbye.

I have been here before, this place where the sheer futility of our existence is so incomprehensible that it becomes nonsense. I have given up on the lie that we are all in on: that anything makes sense. I have dissociated. I know that this is the point where I must try, very hard, to hold onto my body.

Have you ever dissociated?

***

You're sat in a meeting room. It is a hot Wednesday afternoon in September. You have no control over the weather, or the temperature of your office, and the murmur of the radiator is oppressive. Your manager asks a question. You weren't paying attention, you were looking into the cavern, staring inward at the hole. You were peering into it like a tourist at the top of a tall tower, thinking about jumping, knowing you will never jump. You blink and the blankness of your expression slowly fades. 'Excuse me?' You're back in the room.

***

You lie awake on your bed. You are conscious but feel no obligation to speak. Friends, around you, speak about you in the third person as if you cannot hear. Other people feel like the distant waves of a radio frequency you can't quite tune into; you don't respond.

You are lying at the surface of the pool like John Everett Millais' *Ophelia*. Frozen by the cold bath water and the prospect of suicide, you dream to be without a body, but even dreaming reveals your too-present thereness of mind.

There is a man grunting above you. His sweat drips down his philtrum onto your cheek. It is cold, unexpectedly, like the stale rainwater from a drizzly May morning falling onto the white of your scalp. A shock. You stare past him, to the flaking plaster of a rented ceiling. In this moment, your body is as much yours as this flat. You wonder if he would notice if you were dead.

***

Your skin is a rubbery heap of deflated balloons, contorted and opaque, within which you hide bones. Just a bag of bones, limp and ragged on command.

***

Dissociation, 2016–17

It has been sixteen months since I lost my mind. Or, to be more accurate, since my body and mind lost each other. Dissociation is a coping mechanism. It can happen as a reaction to trauma, or to a sudden unexpected change; it can be helped along by a number of drugs, recreational and otherwise. My coping mechanism is to be so avoidant that I dissociate completely.

Recognising dissociation, and its purpose as a coping mechanism for trauma, has made the state seem less terrifying and uncontrollable. We dissociate to get through living all the time. Dog tired, waiting on sore balls of feet after for a delayed train home after an out-of-town business trip. Having sex with someone you've completely lost interest in. Acute heartbreak. It's no more than an extreme form of compartmentalisation; in its most innocuous form, it's simply not concentrating.

I didn't know what to call it until late July of 2017. I was out dancing with friends at what's probably best termed as a cyber-techno-goth-rave with a BDSM aesthetic. It was three or four in the morning, and a friend offered me some keta-mine. It hit instantly, and felled me like a tree. Some time later, I couldn't tell you how long, I returned to myself. It was only later, when discussing it with a therapist, that I recognised the experience as similar to that of my psychosis. 'It sounds as though you dissociated.' I had – the body and mind, and their connection that we take for granted, had disappeared again.

The parallels between the two situations were obvious: in both cases, I had no control or agency over my body. I had recently been through an emotionally exhausting experience. Before going out to the rave, I had said to a friend that I wanted to 'dress like a vampire and feel like a bag of bones', so I had unconsciously primed myself.

It was the differences that were more interesting to me. In the first instance, I knew my body was apart from my mind because I was told about it afterwards. My tissues and muscles and organs had carried on functioning as if I was in control, but 'I' had disappeared, and I don't know where I went. The second time, however, I was conscious of my con-sciousness and sense of self, but it was detached, completely, from my body. I still had my senses, but my perception had disappeared. The voices and the music around me continued to exist and to be heard, but I couldn't identify or distinguish between it. In fact, it was as if it was all my voice. Like a child, I had become unable to identify where I stopped and the world began.

Feeling 'normal' — as though my mind and body matched up — was my immediate priority when I came back to my body on 27 September 2016. I had no recollection of the previous twenty-two days before, where my body had been present, and moving, and talking, but seemingly without the control of my mind. I didn't know what to call it. Amnesia? My parents say they visited me every day. The nurses say I was moved between two wards. I had books and clothes and a backpack of things with me that have disappeared into that black hole, never to be seen again. I was most thrown when my brother said he had visited me in hospital when he'd got back from Rome. I have absolutely no recollection of any of this; there is only blank.

Here is a sketch of how I felt after I returned to earth:

My mind:

I was trapped, almost in amber, on the precipice of this hole. The voices around me billowed, sounding familiar, like the characters that I had in my life prior to my extreme dissociation. They sounded familiar, but there was no comfort to be sought from them. Spending time with friends felt like being in a zoo. Their voices were concerned, but I didn't care. I was so sad, heavy and leaden with the weight of getting through this time.

Meanwhile, body:

A body hanging limp. Its colour is eggshell: conveniently ambiguous. Eggshells come in white and cream and peach and brown and all hues in-between. But the skin itself is like rubber, contorted, the tread of what was once an expression melts away.

The tongue is sodden and flat, a beached whale inside a mouth. It can't move: it has become shapeless and formless because it has forgotten what it means to have form. Those neural pathways created to join syntax with the sinew of connective tissue enabling that mouth, those lips, that slippery tongue, to move to sound and exhilarate and expel some noise with meaning – they've gone. You are abandoned.

Voiceless, limbless, falling, sinking. Nameless. Wordless. Meaningless.

***

It was a dark time. Literally. Winter had started its sunset towards the shortest day of the year and I found myself unemployed and despairing, not feeling myself but not feeling like anything else either. I decided I wanted to use my body, or rather, have it be used. I needed, or felt like I needed, to be doing something with my body without having to think about it. Having sex with strangers seemed like the perfect solution, although my close friends were aghast at the prospect.

But, stubborn and determined, I logged into OKCupid, determined to find anyone to go on a date with. Let me describe to you the state of my dissociation at that time. I was present, in a form, in my body, but I had such physical anxiety that I could barely sit still. My mind and body didn't match – like two different shoes, unbalancing me. My body was wearing heels, and my mind, plimsolls. I wanted to dull the mismatched feeling. On top of the sedatives I'd already been prescribed, I was drinking heavily to 'take the edge off'. By which I mean to push myself towards the dark and dissociative hole where I felt like I belonged.

I found an appropriate match who was more than happy to oblige me in taking him out for a drink. We met in a bar which had a really soothing ambiance, but, still, in preparation, I drank three alcoholic drinks and took two diazepam. We had sex that night. At that time, sex was the only stimulant I could bear. Having my body moved from one position to another, by another, let me escape myself. I felt like a doll. He moved my arms, my legs, one at a time. Not with any yogic fluidity, but with an almost aggressive commotion.

Now, looking back to that evening, and the gaps in my memory, I would say I was frightened at the speed at which I attempted to resume normal life, including dating. In particular, I feel that I was lacking the guardianship that my mind owes my body. I was having sex to dissociate and to ignore the fact that the state of my mind was a disorganised wreck, the only help to which I could give was sex that I didn't really want to have.

Yet, as I grew stronger, the sex became less of a dissociation-avoidance process and more of an activity that I came to enjoy. I came to dislike the man I had begun sleeping with, but I had rediscovered myself and expanded my boundaries, willingly, from the 'bad patch' that I'd been having. I met a new man, a new friend, and we had sex. In that encounter I tried a number of new activities that I wouldn't have considered had it not been for the period of dissociated sex that I'd been having.

***

February 2017 – a green dress, to which I'm attached

Clothes played a key part in making me feel myself rather than my disconnected other self again, as did a sexual experience in February 2017. I met my new friend in my green dress, the one I'd bought for three pounds on Camberwell Road. It has a hole in the back and shows off my best self. I last wore it at a barbecue in the summer before and after I was ill. I laughed performatively and did that thing with my voice that I've picked up that makes everyone think I'm flirting with them. Because I am. My ex-boyfriend was at the party with the first girl he'd slept with after me. My dress said: don't pity me. I'm free and you are insignificant.

I wore that dress as a pick-me-up. I was miserable, barely employed, spending hours not writing and instead thinking about when I could kill myself. I decided that it could be that Friday, the one before I met him. I got the DLR in the morning from Deptford, from the house of another insignificant, though I'd desperately wanted to stay. I didn't want to come back; to 'home', to emptiness, to disconnection from the four women I shared my space with, who I should be able to tolerate. I didn't tell anyone, not even my closest friend. I just set the train in motion. I remember feeling hopeless when the transaction for my hopelessness drugs didn't go through. And dumb. £300. That was when I decided I would make my suicide kit. (I haven't yet, don't worry.)

So you can see why I needed a pick-me-up, that green dress covered in velvety scales, exposing my back and my best self. I bought some cocaine and S and I got silly in my room. She was a good friend to aspire to be, a protagonist. We went to see Avalon and Lena in a refurbished working men's club. They'd upholstered it to appeal to people like us, with hip

81

young bar staff and bottled craft beer.

He was the only one dancing. He looked like an Onix – the Pokémon, not the stone – the grey and black of his stripes and stones with his shoulders curved back and his neck curved forward. No one else was dancing and he didn't care. He was a hot mess; a beautiful boy in a beautiful dress. A pick-me-up. I exposed my best self, my connected self, my real self, with the help of the jade-green dress and the cocaine.

What was my line? 'Your outfit is amazing.' He lived in Bow, it made sense to get a taxi. 'Let's smoke a joint,' he said. 'And have some tea.' He took a pause to throw up. I still didn't know if he liked girls, or me, so I got undressed.

I thought he was kinkier than he is because of that first time. A boy in a dress with a shoebox full of sex toys. I assumed he knew the ropes (forgive my crudeness). But really, he was just open to vulnerability. Open to openness (again, forgive my crudeness). I slept with him for the experience of sleeping with a boy in a dress with a shoebox full of sex toys under his bed, something that would only happen in my pick-me-up dress. Green, with the exposed back. Showing off my best self.

***

April 2018

I remember that evening of over a year ago often now. Parts of my life resemble that of the time before I met my best friend in my best dress. I have to remember that there was a time before now that looks rather a lot like now, and that I got through it, to find myself here. I have come to accept that there is a part of me that cannot accept the absurdity of the world we inhabit and that on one level, interactions, however meaningful or from however beloved a connection, feel futile. The shape of things will always seem peculiar, and detached, and it's difficult not to constantly pursue absurdity, or detachment. It's difficult not to chase stories so that I can remember them afterwards.

It is with a reluctance that I have come to accept that I will

82

often feel somewhat other: my body will often feel as though it is being operated by someone other than myself, forcing and willing me to continue when my mind is somewhere else, uninvested in its outcome. My mind is the guardian of a beautiful thing, my body, and I must cooperate. The corporeality of it all sickens me sometimes, but I'm still bound to protect it. It's my bag of bones. It's mine.

Bleach Wax Shave Repeat
Marta Bausells

1.

I recently calculated that I have spent more than five thousand pounds on getting body hair removed, and that's considering that I go long periods without waxing amd that I was rounding down on my calculations: it's probably much more. This doesn't include visits to my hairdresser. Head-hair can be left for another time, in which I'll tell you all about the several grey hairs I pulled out this morning.

Over the last month alone, I have paid to get hair waxed off of four different areas: upper lip, underarm, bikini line, full legs. Alternative euphemisms include: moustache, armpits, pubic hair. I plucked my eyebrows myself (just a bit, I like them bold) and the space between them, and groomed them with a mini-comb and a treatment called 'little eyebrow monsters'. I pulled out a lone black hair that grows out of a beauty mark below my lower lip. I bleached my arm hair, which I had disastrously decided to wax for my thirtieth birthday party and later grew out twice as thick.

2.

Something has been troubling me: I am angry at the money and time hair removal costs me, which I could be spending on writing, projects, art, pleasure. Most of all, I am angry that I can't stop. This should ideally be a question of: do it or don't, and whatever you choose, don't feel bad.

I don't want to conform to what I see as misogynistic beauty norms. This means there are occasions when I have decided to go all-natural. I often do it for a few weeks, sometimes months – but I always end up caving. Weddings are my weak spot: I am yet to attend one in all my glory. Gender can often feel like a performance for many of us, and I sometimes take the path of least resistance. I am also a cis, able-bodied, white woman, and consider myself to be incredibly privileged to call this an issue.

This issue has created tension in my relationship. My partner prefers women who do not have leg hair. He is ashamed of his 'retrograde' and 'not advanced' desires – his words – and I am a hypocrite, because I admonish him and have gone as far as questioning our relationship because of it. But, I must admit, I too prefer my legs smooth and hair-free.

3.

One summer night in London, a famous American actress arrives to a movie premiere in the West End. She's wearing a shiny mid-length red dress and black sandals, her hair in a nondescript bun, and she is all smiles. She's the perfect incarnation of the American life my generation was so effectively spoon-fed – more like IV-dripped – through popular culture in the 90s: she has a girl-next-door air about her, a friendly, welcoming face; her beauty is unattainable all the same, but we don't know it.

As she gets out of a black car, she acts surprised and elated at the awaiting fans' hysterical screams, and stands for a few seconds in front of the crowd in apparent disbelief. Then she starts waving at them, and her armpit hair peeks out of her short sleeves.

As she walks inside the multiplex cinema, a male reporter approaches her and, of all the questions he could pose, he asks: '[The male lead] says you're a great kisser. He's a bit of a charmer, isn't he?' She doesn't blink an eye, pouts lightly and replies with a nonchalant smile reminiscent of old-school Hollywood stars: 'Yes he is, but he's very English that way.' She walks away.

It's 1999, the movie is *Notting Hill*, and the actress is Julia Roberts, perfectly recreating the celebrity character she played in the movie. One might guess that she had no idea the very inconsequential decision of not shaving would conjure such an intense flurry of attention and commentary. When asked about the incident afterwards, she reportedly said: 'On a day-to-day basis, I don't think about my armpits'.

Perhaps everyone else does it for her. Google 'celebrities with armpit hair' today (19 years later): those lists keep getting published by the media, every year, and she is invariably
86

top of the list. I even found a picture of Roberts in a news piece about a Modigliani exhibition at the TATE Modern.

4.

Frida Kahlo's facial hair, together with the indigenous Mexican symbolism in her work, is arguably one of the most well-known retorts to cultural imperialism and the male gaze in art history. Many male artists have depicted women's hair in their work – Goya's *La maja desnuda*, Modigliani's languid women, Courbet's glorious painting *L'Origine du monde*. However, Kahlo did something else altogether. She self-selected, highlighted, chose to paint herself in her own way. Her brow and moustache, present in both her realist and surreal self-portraits, were signs of agency over her body. A body that was failing and ailing her in so many ways.

5.

Twenty-five percent of British women reportedly do not shave their armpit hair, which might suggest that fewer and fewer women care. However, the data does not discern if this is consistent across different ethnicities. Nevertheless, we are still obsessed with women's bodies, and how they maintain them.

In 1996, Drew Barrymore revealed her hairy armpits when she posed for photographer Mario Sorrenti in front of giant cacti and a fading magenta wall. Barrymore wears a translucent chiffon dress while delicately touching her head with her arms, one of which is arched behind her head like a convoluted classical statue. She has consistently attended events throughout her career unshaven. Juliette Lewis, Lady Gaga, the actresses from *Girls*, Penélope Cruz are some of the women in the public eye that have done the same.

Still, I continue my googling and immediately find an on-line list, published in 2017 (I triple check the year just to make sure), of '15 Celebrities Who Forgot to Shave' on a publication I won't give the publicity to. Their writer shames each woman listed for their 'shocking personal grooming over-sights' and laments: 'Celebrities are human just like the rest of us, but you would think with that much cash in the bank they would never leave the house looking anything less than perfect – however, this isn't always the case.'

Other times it's more benign-sounding, but the message is always the same: this is abnormal and worthy of attention and scrutiny. These women are either so wild and sexual that they aren't smoothing up their bodies for society (see Madonna and her pits in the 80s), or worse, they don't care – they are rebels, queer women, outside the norm anyway (see Patti Smith's *Easter* album cover). In the latter case, it is often depicted as a hippy thing of the past deserving no attention.

6.

It is not conceivable that our "good girls" do this, which is why Roberts's pits became iconic – at least for young girls like me, for whom mainstream pop culture was a lifeline, her movies an obsession, and her look not a crazy one to compare to.

When actress Lola Kirke attended the Golden Globes with unshaven pits in 2017, she got death threats online. Paris Jackson and Lourdes Leon (Michael Jackson and Madonna's daughters respectively) were both critiqued when they were photographed with underarm hair, at 18 and 20 years old; in Leon's case, while at the beach with her friends.

7.

Jackson took to her Instagram Stories to express her surprise, in comments so similar to Roberts's two decades earlier: 'I didn't realise that people were going to get so upset over my armpit hair. I didn't realise that was such an issue. It is so funny. People are really mad.'

Haters gonna hate, for sure, and the internet has given them a platform – but why are people so mad? Have we made no progress?

Let's not forget that we're here talking only about armpits. Often said to be 'making a comeback,' armpit hair is usually seen in otherwise sanitised, hairless celebrity bodies. They don't have facial hair. Their legs are smoothly shaved.

88

Hair in other body parts gets more – or rather, even more shaming – attention. Here are two sample headlines that followed actress and comedian Mo'nique's appearance to the Golden Globes and the NAACP awards with natural legs in 2015: 'Mo'nique explains why she finally started shaving her legs' (*USA Today*); 'Wait, what? Mo'Nique says hubby can cheat, loves her hairy legs' (*NY Daily News*) – connecting her body hair with sexual promiscuity.

8.

In our culture, what we do with our hair is intertwined with identity, culture and societal norms. For adolescent girls, it is often the first way – together with their period and the myriad ways they must hide it – they are introduced to what having a woman's body means, what rules it has to follow to be acceptable – and how it is their responsibility to make it live up to that standard.

New York-based Pakistani-American artist Ayqa Khan makes art depicting women of colour enjoying life, subverting pop culture iconography. Normalising body hair plays a big part in her artworks. In her prints, brown girls lounge at the beach, rollerblade or skateboard.

In one piece, 'International Women's Day', a woman sits at an American diner sipping juice, wearing sunglasses; a tote bag sits next to her on the floor that reads 'feminist as fuck,' an Audre Lorde (spelled 'Lore') book sits on the table, and the word 'halal' is written on the wall in a neon sign next to a picture of Angela Davis and Betty Boop, re-invented as a brown woman with a hairy body, a mirror of the hairy arms and legs of the image's protagonist. It is an image saturated with power and joy.

Khan is not just combatting the pressures for women to remove their body hair, she's also exposing the racial biases behind this societal norm: hair removal is often considered another imposed way to reach whiteness. In a piece about Khan's work, Naz Riahi, an Iranian-American entrepreneur, talked about how the connotations of body hair among brown and white women are remarkably different:

> *Our discomfort with the body hair, especially*
> *that of black and brown women is not just in-*
> *fluenced by patriarchy but is also a remnant of*
> *colonialism. This is a system in which we were*
> *taught that fairness, lightness, whiteness and all*
> *that comes with it—blue eyes, blonde hair, less*
> *body hair—is more beautiful, appealing, better.*[1]

Writer Fariha Roisin commented, in the same piece:

> *White women not removing body hair is quite*
> *laughable to me. White women don't have the*
> *history, or the baggage of growing up with visi-*
> *ble body hair, so their announcement of it, or po-*
> *litical positionality of it, seems insincere. Many*
> *brown folks, including me, were bullied growing*
> *up for being too hairy. When there's no history*
> *of subjugation or even cultural abuse, it seems*
> *premature to align yourself with something that*
> *essentially has no consequence for you, irrespec-*
> *tive of how vocal you are with it.*[2]

9.

Instagram seems to have opened the floodgates of another interesting phenomenon: white-girl 'art' of hyper-feminine fluffiness. Recently, the feminist art criticism duo The White Pube, formed of Gabrielle de la Puente and Zarina Muhammad, wrote:

> *we cannnnnot be here as feminists in 2017 still*
> *making art about PERIODS, BODY HAIR,*
> *THE COLOUR PINK AND BEAUTY STAND-*
> *ARDS. Fuck with the system itself and get struc-*

1   Bursa Erkara, 'Feminist Body Hair is Rarely an Option for Midde Eastern Women' (*i-D Vice*, 2017)< https://i-d.vice.com/en_uk/article/xwd-d4q/feminist-body-hair-is-rarely-an-option-for-middle-eastern-women >

2   Ibid.

> *tural, critical, political. Activate ur aesthetics.[3]*

The post unsurprisingly generated a heated debate, with some commenters taking issue with it. The White Pube wrote further:

> '*I completely support [people's] right to make the art they wanna make, good and bad, 'relevant' or not etc etc, go for it. Everyone's art is most relevant to them isn't it. But what I'm sayin with this tweet is that I think it [would] be better to be structural in your art activity rather than tepidly aesthetic. To [be] political rather than faux rad in [your] prettiness. [...] Personally I fuck with something that changes the reasons we even needed to make that art in the first place*'.

I can certainly think of popular Instagram artists whose entire project consists of presenting languid women (and their body parts) as ethereal, flowery pastel fruits, ready to be commercialised and made marketable. I feel like this isn't too far from the kind of co-opting that has led to brands like Topshop putting the word 'Feminist' on t-shirts, a perverse cynicism if one takes a second to think about their company's policies and how they may affect their women employees, for instance.

10.

I don't think femininity should equal hairlessness, and I don't want to want to be hairless. We must ask ourselves: what are we seeing – who is showing it to us, and what does it mean?

Beside our personal work, what needs to happen for internalised patriarchy-trained ideals and desires to change to match our rational beliefs? Representation is key, always: you can't aspire to be what you don't see. Is this simply a

3   <https://twitter.com/thewhitepube/status/933646752749629440>

question of seeing a wide spectrum of hairiness in women enough times? Is it that the more unshaved legs we all see, the closer we'll get to accepting the agency and autonomy of others to do as they please, when they please?

11.

Eventually, I realise that my 'hair / no hair' wanderings are just another distraction. I realise the privilege I have to call this an issue, and even with hair, I may pass as what is deemed acceptable. As a white woman, can growing out your hair even be a political statement? Is it a small visible way to say 'fuck you' to the patriarchy or, like Roisin pointed out, is that a delusion?

For many of us, gender lends itself to performance. At times I am perceived as very feminine, which is easy for me to perform. At other times, I want to shave my head, grow out all my body hair, wear a suit and no make up. But I reject those limiting concepts of femininity / masculinity in the first place. I long for a day in which not only is everything more fluid, but the very definition of femininity includes body hair. Lots of it, in all places, in bodies of all shapes and colours. So why am I still waxing before attending parties, even if I'm not feeling it – simply because I want to have a fun time and not be scrutinised by strangers; looked at awkwardly, maybe commented on behind my back, by acquaintances I don't particularly care about; maybe considered rude by people whose value system I refuse?

I am a woman from the south of Europe, potentially with much more hair than other women from Northern European countries. My attending a wedding as hairy as can be might not change anything. But I might as well try. How dare I hide behind the looks of acceptability, when I already have it easier than many? Insignificant as the gesture might be, it will at least accomplish something for me personally: It might force me to stop wasting energy worrying about this, and free myself to be concerned with working to make every space more inclusive for people of all gender identities and ethnicities, for whom the luxury of this choice is not an option.

A Body Found

Kasim Mohammed

[Content note: eating disorders, fatphobia, weight loss]

Aishwarya Rai. That name is Bollywood royalty, made even more so by her marriage to the Bachchan family, a group of people who shine the brightest in the South Asian film industry. Light-skinned and beautiful, she soared through the echelons of the Bollywood hierarchy in the late 1990s and early 2000s, making film after film. Her name and face have been attached to the most iconic of Bollywood films. If you utter the word *Devdas*, a 2002 Bollywood film about two lovers who ultimately destroy one another, which traumatised an entire generation with its brutal ending, anyone with brown skin will immediately conjure her face.

There was often gossip about her during those years, at the height of her career. About the clothes she wore, about the clothes she didn't wear, the people she was with, the people she wasn't with, but it was the gossip about her marriage to Abhishek Bachchan that was important in my house and my family. My mother, in particular, hated the union. She said that Aishwarya had sold out, that she had only married for the name, that it was a loveless marriage. I said nothing, for I didn't know enough to have an opinion. I kept quiet, a soundboard for my mother's rage about something that didn't affect her.

And then, in 2011, Aishwarya disappeared. She didn't appear at red carpet events anymore. She went into hiding. Gossip leaked that she was pregnant with her first child, the result of the consummation of her 'loveless marriage'. My mother grew incensed: how could she do that? How could she put her body through that? *How could she?*

My father, on the other hand, was a huge Aishwarya fan. His reasoning was straightforward: he enjoyed her face, so he watched her films. He cared nothing about the politics of her marriage or her pregnancy; he only cared that she continued to make films and look beautiful in them.

Aishwarya had her child and returned to the cameras. And

she did so as a woman who had put on weight. Unsurprisingly, her transformation had been captured in an endless stream of photos by the paparazzi. Her normally angular face was coated in fat, her cheeks had widened, her neck was thick, her stomach round beneath her clothes. She was no longer the sexy young woman that you might imagine yourself with late in the evening; she now looked the part of the homely woman who might offer you food and warmth for a night, who you might talk to about your problems, but who you would never want to take to bed. She became the internet's 'Indian Aunty'.

My father asked me to show him these new pictures of his favourite; when he took the phone from me, his face filled with disgust and curiosity. 'How could she let this happen to her?' he asked me, as though I was an expert on the subject. I said nothing again, because I had no knowledge on the matter, though I did wonder if it had something to do with the fact that she had just given birth to a human being.

Aishwarya went into hiding again after those photos, and there was no more speculation in our house, for we all knew why this time. I could only wonder about how she felt when she went home. Did she cry? Did she eat? Did she start picking at food, only to throw it across the room? Did she rage and shout? Did she destroy things?

Months later, she appeared at the Cannes Film Festival. Her post-pregnancy figure had been sucked away. Dressed in a skin-tight dress, she posed, hands on hips, lips tarred with red, and she stared straight at the cameras as if to say, 'Isn't this what you wanted?'

She was thin, and the world rejoiced, because the world loves thin people.

My father smiled when he looked at the new photos. He said little, but he smiled.

***

The table at my grandmother's house is all but groaning under the weight. Chaval. Samoseh. Pakoreh. Kebabs. Rasmalai. Kheer. Bottles of Coca-Cola are lined up underneath the dinner table. Plastic cups and plastic plates and plastic cutlery. A piece of plastic wrap lines the table, protecting the wood from stains, and another one on the floor of the living room. A giant chocolate cake bought from Costco and its counterpart, a sponge cake lightly dusted with icing, top off the feast.

I stand before the food. Ramadan has just finished. My stomach, which has spent the previous thirty days growling with hunger, is ready to go.

This is the summer of my final year at college. This is the last summer that I will be able to look at myself and not immediately be filled with hate at what I see. This is the summer before I see my body distort, like I am the living reflection of a funny mirror, bending my body into something I do not recognise.

When my grandmother says I can, I sit at the table and reach for the food. I pile my plate as high as it goes. There is a moment before we place the first morsel of food into our mouths, silence as we appreciate the food we have been given. This meal, breaking our fast, is a joyful one, and my siblings and I laugh while we eat. Because the food tastes great, and it always has, and it always will.

***

There is an unspoken truth in my house: my mother always needs to lose weight.

When she was younger, she was a runner. Her lithe body pushed her past her limits and through finish lines and over banners. She won trophies at school; she might even have been able to train as a professional. But she was married off to a man she had barely met right after she finished her exams, and a year later, she gave birth to my older sister. And so began her descent into fatness, and a hatred of her own body.

She is now forty-three, twenty years older than me, and she is always dieting, or trying to diet, or talking about how she needs to diet. Sometimes she will restrict the food she allows herself, monitoring herself. She will go to the gym, run on treadmills for as long as she can, returning home sweaty but refreshed. She will eat fruit and she will tell us not to buy chocolate, concerned that she will eat it if we do. She says she won't get takeaway with us. And then there are times when she dives into the world of gluttony, without a single look backwards. Afterwards, she'll hate herself, and there is an atmosphere of bitterness in our house.

She is up, and then she is down, and then she is up, and then she is down.

I remember the first time I started feeling something akin to hatred of my body. I was fifteen and I was in the gym with the other boys in school. I was a little chubby. Not huge, not obese, but there was a small lump of fat on my stomach. I'd never really noticed it, but that day, as I changed clothes, I happened to glimpse one of the other boys. He was tall, and he was light-skinned, and he had a six-pack.

I stared at his stomach, and then I looked down at my own, and I quickly covered myself with my clothes. I felt shame trickle down my back, embarrassment light itself in my cheeks, humiliation in the pit of my fat fat fat stomach.

That night, I went home and I prodded at the lump. I wanted to get rid of it, but I didn't know how.

I thought of asking my older sister, who had been chubby but was now thin, for help. Her cheekbones were like knives, her bones seemed to be leaping to freedom from her skin. I knew that she worked out in her room, lifting weights and doing push-ups, sit-ups, whatever kind of -ups she needed. I wanted to go to her, to ask her what I could do, but I couldn't, because she would laugh at me.

Because it was normal for girls to want to be thin, but it wasn't for boys.

So I started to work out a little myself, borrowing her weights when she wasn't looking. I started to notice men more on TV, their gleaming bodies, their muscles, the size of their arms, the relative flatness of their stomachs. I compared their bodies to mine and wondered if working out wasn't enough.

And so I began to skip lunch. Less food meant that I would be thin, right? I started to halve my breakfast, some-
96

times leaving it altogether. My mother never knew; she was never awake in the morning. When I returned from school and she would offer me a snack before mosque, I'd tell her that I'd eaten a big lunch at school so I wasn't hungry. Some days, my only meal would be dinner.

It didn't work. The small lump of fat on my stomach was still there. I began to despise it, poking the lump as though if I caused it enough pain, it might get up off my body and leave.

I watch an episode of *Glee* where the boys are working out in the gym. One of the boys, a blond blue-eyed boy, tugs at the skin on his non-existent stomach. He says he is fat. I hate him.

I watch an episode of *Doctor Who* where a pill makes people's fat leap off their stomachs and run for safety. I want that pill so badly, I can almost taste it.

I watch *Captain America* and I see a small thin man become a muscle-bound superhero, and I want it. I want all of it.

Around the mid to late 2000s, this trend of muscles and low body fat percentages crossed the sea, and landed in Bollywood. I had grown up watching Bollywood heroes who bore something of a resemblance to the men in my family. They were soft around the stomach, around the jaw, around everywhere, and they had the same hair on their body as my father did. But suddenly, they were hairless too. Suddenly, they had muscles too. Suddenly, they were everything I couldn't be too.

Wherever I turned, the worlds around me showed me perfect men, and I wasn't one.

But I was also surrounded by men who weren't perfect. My father, who was fat. My uncle, who was fat. My cousins, who were fat. Here were the people I saw every day, looking the same way I did. I tried, time and again, to find the peace they clearly possessed.

But no matter how I tried to find happiness, it always eluded me.

***

University promised a fresh start.

I would be able to go and better myself, better my body and my mind, away from my family, studying English, my favourite subject.

At home, my mother made traditional food, which was rich and fatty. Curries laced with oil, chapattis covered in butter, desserts filled with sugar. We were fed the most opulent of food and, like the kings of past, we grew fat and large and lazy.

But the second my family drove away, I realised that I may have eaten this food but I had little idea as to how to make it. Rather than learn how to use a pot or the science behind spices, I turned to my local Sainsbury's and I bought food straight from the freezer. Pizzas and chips and fish fingers and garlic bread. They went in the oven and twenty minutes later, I would have a meal. It was simple, wonderful. I went to McDonald's, discovered Nando's, found the ease of food delivered right to your door.

That first year of university was quite possibly the happiest I have ever felt. Away from my mother, I could find pleasure in food. Away from a voice that constantly spoke of food with hatred, I felt great. I no longer shied away from it; I embraced it. I ate what I wanted, and I didn't notice the changes it made to my body. I didn't care.

But the fun ended when I returned home that summer, and everyone said: 'Wow, you got fat!'

The moment I heard this, the world closed in on me. I couldn't breathe, my chest tightened. I looked at myself, and I finally saw it: I had ballooned. My clothes didn't fit me, my stomach pushed against the threads. My jaw had disappeared into folds of fat. My cheeks were filled with food. I felt disgusting, ugly, grotesque. I needed to stop.

It seemed everyone in my family had a comment about my

body lined up. They told me I was huge, that they couldn't believe I was the same person, that they had never imagined I would end up this way. I shied away from family events, didn't want to leave the house, didn't want to face people who would throw words at me like darts, who I felt would try to grab my fleshy body with their hands, pull at it as if I was a doll made out of clay for them to shape and mould.

When I got back to university, I joined the gym. I ran on treadmills, listening to pop music, miming the words. I lifted weights at the machine, up and down, never rested. I went four times a week, five on a good one, six on a great one. But I would find myself drawn to food, and whatever calories I burned at the gym, I put back on. The gluttonous love I had formed of food in the first year of university stuck to me like the fat stuck to my bones.

I cried about it when I was alone. I poked and prodded myself, bruising the skin on my stomach and my thighs, where all the fat collected. I pulled my cheeks back in the mirror, imagining what I might look like if only I was thinner. I thought happiness existed there, at the other end of the scales.

In the second summer of university, I tried to use Ramadan to lose weight. I thought fasting for thirty days would be a good way to drop the pounds and find the 'real' me under the fat. But Ramadan is a celebration of togetherness and of eating. Once the sun's light ebbed away, I devoured the food put in front of me. By the time the month was over, I had gained even more weight. I was a magnet for fat.

And yet, I spoke to no one about the way I was feeling. I had been taught to think that feeling bad about your body was something that only women and teenage girls felt. Men, I was taught, would never trouble themselves with something as frivolous as appearances. My father didn't feel this way; he'd been getting fatter and fatter for years, an upward line on a graph, cheerfully claiming that he 'couldn't' lose weight. My uncles didn't feel this way. My cousins didn't feel this way.

So why was I feeling this way?

I couldn't find an answer to the question, so I answered it by torturing myself more. I continued to hate myself. I continued to stay quiet.

Because how could I turn to the men around me and confess my shortcomings as one of them? I already didn't fit the mould. I was sensitive and weak. I used my spare time to read books, not play football. I cared little about cars and even less about porn. I was an anomaly, and in the confines of their binary convictions, if I wasn't like them, I was like the women.

Women, in their eyes, were weak. They were shallow and vapid, mean and cruel. They weren't smart, they weren't funny, they weren't talented. Success didn't line their pockets with money, because they had no idea how to court it. As far as the men in my life were concerned, women were only good for the kitchen and the bedroom.

But women were also soft and kind, they were the ones to turn to when you had a problem and needed advice. My mother was the person I told my worries to, not my father. My grandmother the one I hugged, not my grandfather. My aunties the ones I went with for days out, not my uncles.

Men were strong and cruel because of it; women were weak and kind because of it.

And I had to be the former, not the latter, so I kept my mouth shut.

***

I left university over two years ago. In that time, I have moved twice. I have found different methods of keeping fit, of running, of working out with exercise videos, of working out at the gym. I have found a way to balance my love of food with my self-image. I am learning to accept my body, knowing that I 'want' rather than 'need' to lose weight.

I sometimes think about my sister, the one with the razor-sharp cheekbones. I have since learned that my sister was bulimic, that she took laxatives to get her weight down and keep it there, that fingers would find the hollow of her throat and push down. That she hated her body just as much as I hated mine, that she sought thinness in the butts of cigarettes and the white gleam of toilet bowls.

She tried to find her body, and I tried to find mine.

I am at the better part of my journey now, but even so, I cannot own my body the way I want. Because I was once 'too fat', my body will forever be up for public consumption. I am never too far away from a comment about it, never too far from someone using their words to colour me in.

My family look at me now and they say, 'Wow, you look good.' I am supposed to reply to this with humility, with self-deprecation, with an exclamation of, 'There's still more to do!' I am supposed to say that I used to look bad. And they'll take it one step further, telling me that still, even now, I am not enough. That I am less than.

Aunties will tell me that I look good enough to get married now, but they poke at my receding hairline that I have inherited from my father and tell me I should do it soon, before I go entirely bald. They tell me that I should find someone now before I start getting fat again. They tell me that I should go to the gym more, to get muscles, because 'that's what girls want these days'. They peel me apart with their words, and they don't offer to put me back together again.

But these words do not have the same effect on me as they once did. I have learned the difference between the want and the need. I have learned the difference between punishment and discipline. I smile at them, I nod, I walk away. Because I am now ok with finding the joy in eating, and with finding the joy in working out.

There are still moments that make me feel as though I am part of the problem. A cousin will look at me with eyes wide with amazement and she will ask, 'How did you lose so much weight?' I will shrug, say something about the gym and food. I tell her the truth, but it is not the truth that she wants. I can see it in the line of her lip, the distrust in her tone. She wants me to tell her that there is a special way to lose weight, that I have stumbled upon the solution that will grant her happiness.

I do not know how to tell her that I am on the same journey.

I do not know how to tell her that I am unsure if I will ever find the answer.

I do not know how to step outside of this conversation.

***

I belong to a culture of food. I belong to a culture of good food, not food that is good for you. Of oil and sugar, of butter and milk, of fat. I belong to a people who are predisposed to develop type 2 diabetes, to have higher blood pressure, to have high cholesterol, to have heart attacks because our veins are filled with the food that we eat.

I belong to a culture that is hypocritical, one that will attack your body with one hand whilst feeding it with the other. Parents do not often, if ever, censor their conversations around their children. Mothers talk about weight, and fathers talk about the gym. Single people talk in kilogrammes and pounds, and teenagers alter their images with Snapchat filters and angles. Everyone is obsessed with their bodies, and the way bodies look, and the way bodies should look. Perfect ideals are thrown around in everyday conversation, from all cultures around me. From the white people at work to my black friends to my brown family.

In this, we are all Aishwarya Rai. Except, like my mother often says, her lips a snarl, her tone bitter; 'We can't fucking afford to look like that.'

Well, I no longer feel the need to.

Etxeberria
Jake Elliott

1.

Sundays, one Sunday after another. It's a problem of perception, I'm aware of that. Nothing ever changes. I'm aware that
it's a problem of perception. A different run up, perhaps. I had
brought people into the world and in return they had waited.
They had waited for my past to outweigh my future. I had
brought people into the world and they had waited until I was
really quite distracted. Then, against my will, they had moved
me to a clinic. For geriatrics. As if that wasn't enough, and it
was, it was more than enough, the clinic was not ready. You
do understand? Under construction. I was its first resident;
I was the clinic's only resident and of course I was, after all,
they hadn't asked to be born.

Outside was out of bounds, so I gazed through glass at the
plants, at the gardeners and their wide-brimmed hats. In fact,
when I looked out I looked in, because that room, like all the
vacant others, faced an atrium and a mess of shrubs and soil.

Flailing trowels lent quick sentience to the glass. But when
was 'quick' ever long enough? Inch- thick glass of course, to
block out the noise. And I made all sorts of noise. In English,
French, Spanish and Basque. For the record, I was grateful for
the glass. Floor to ceiling, sagging net curtains, it granted me a
kind of vocation, overdubbing the figures outside.

In the courtyard, cigarette buds powdered plates of afternoon melon while the ache of the day bloomed within. Gusts
combed myrtle and vetiver, disturbed the wine-bottle pond
and its elusive tench. Mature plants, root balls scrim-bagged,
loitered for treatment, awaited the gardener's life-giving

103

graves. The species had done their growing and so, as in the Jardin des Plantes, adult echeveria would differ with *l'immortelle des dunes*, dabs of yucca and the native ekilore. If the exclusion of saplings and seeds wasn't enough, see-through sacks of Biscay mud, the supposed source of the clinic's allure, forgive me, slouched like majestic shits on plate glass.

Between transparent panes, Julene, the doctor, slipped into the courtyard. She pointed straight at me.

'Look over there! Madame in her window, as ever, south side of the garden.'

They did not look. Out of bounds she gestured and the gardeners' heads swung to her, each one wearing the same pink grin it was born with. Enthralled, their dibbles dropped; they had eyes only for the doctor.

'... Look at her though. Desire is usually fading at her age. Not in Madame Elixabete. Far too pervasive. No discernible end, no locatable source; it comes from everywhere, all over her. It takes too many forms to be simply got rid of.'

I am ashamed to admit I said her words aloud,

'I exist immensely for her, you see and the turmoil I create, it gives her, she thinks, some sort of right over me. She is convinced she deserves me.'

The doctor threw her arms in the air, then tapped her watch. Her mouth moved, but behind the glass, no message was made. For better or worse, I resumed. I made it, slipping sounds between her lips, one word at a time.

'Madame needs to feel her wanting work. Do you understand? She likes my visits. So I avoid them. I allow her to feel her wanting build in the delay. For her my consultations are a
104

dream. It is your job to provide sustenance through her waking hours. Spores, stamens, carpels...'

She puffed her cheeks, frowned.

'Incidentally, she is not sick, not even at all, so carry on with your work; do what I am doing, keep her desire in sight, give her this garden differently each day. Work her up. See what happens.'

With a sleeve she wiped sweat from her brow.

In my room, I did the same. I said, '*Mademoiselle médecin -*' I looked up. She'd disappeared into the glass.

It was a pleasure taken in place of those denied. You could call it that. The violet heavens above me, the city's vivid tips. The surfers in the bay, skimming the point, slicing open the water flesh, splashing about in white spume. By which I mean to say, Julene, the doctor. The feeling of her, all over and inside me. Her breath on my stomach, basting my body in syrup-wet sap. A crumbled baserri, damp cot, mattress stained and the shuddering... excuse me.

Dumb wonder was never my particular way. Even at my age, conjecture, speculation, the livelier forms of not knowing. Well, they're a little more me. A lover told me once, that the essential quality of any tool is whether it has the dimensions to handle your questions. And yet. That may've been Helen Pashgian. Do you know the Light and Space artists? Another time, perhaps. I mean to say that I possess the dimensions to deal with my own questions. More than that. Things have little potency in themselves; I've tended to confer it.

Regardless, I slurped the oat flower tea and closed my eyes.

105

2.

They will need to think again about the bathrooms. Too many cords. I pulled the red one accidentally and the orderlies burst in. They lifted me past the bed, back to my chair by the glass. They smoothed my skirt.

Assumptions have been made by these younger people. My life has filled, brimmed, leaked onto theirs and now they have to stop me from seeping all over the place. I'm not talking about urine, you do understand that?

They stood in front of my chair. Two barren torsos. Mint scrubs. I imagine they offered me sheep's curd and macadamias, asked if I was 'doing ok'. All I heard was,

'You'll need to try harder if you want Julene.'

It was dark. The door clicked to. The gardeners had gone and in the borders, molten bulbs lit leaves underneath; the pond sent chartreuse plaits flouncing up the panes and vacant rooms gawped in the shadows.

'...is what I've always said. It is. It's what I've always said about her. It is. I shan't say it again. She's given up. She is – No. Please, let me say it. She's decided to call it a day, far too early at that, and she'll regret it. Letting them stick us up here in a fucking sanatorium.'

Rapid talk from nowhere. I looked at my lips reflected in the window. They were still.

'You've made your thoughts on that abundantly clear. Now, what about the doctor? What next?'

'She is all we have.'

106

'*Is she all we have? We do not have her.*'

'*We are in the process of having her.*'

'*It is underway?*'

'*It is.*'

'*Having her is having her want us.*'

'*It is.*'

'*And we are in the process of having her want us.*'

'*We are already having it. A little bit.*'

'*But it isn't enough.*'

'*Soon it will be time for more.*'

You do understand then? These are the words that I heard.

I turned my good ear to the wall and drove my palms over my lap, over swollen beige veins. Portuguese ceramics were all the rage when I was young, Bordallo Pinheiro in particular. And so, a skirt, embroidered with savoy sheets; cabbage leaves, dimpled, like citrus peel. At two patches in the fabric, my fingers worked the fibres and troubled a memory.

Getaria. Txakoli with the sculptor. Flushed, babbling the booze, scowling, working his way up, under the cloth, under the plates, under the cabbage leaves. I thought it was a joke until my knees slammed the table, pressed hard against the grain. He fumbled, fussed, hot cheek at my neck and spat the 'Shhhhhhhh!' hard, into my ear.

I lapsed.

White dahlias in their vase swayed the either/or of his pursuit and beyond the bay window, a dismal sea did nothing. I caught my breath, 'That's enough, Ibai!' and my voice, too loud, disgraced him. Wine bubbles crackled the silence. He drove me home.

In the window, in my face, in the dark, I could see my need to be needed ebbing away. And I did not want it gone. I could see a younger me, understanding how she wanted to be needed. And in the reflection, the distance between the women, who were me, collapsed. In the glass, I was still the teenager in the cabbage patch skirt, bored by the way I was wanted by men; perched in a dim kitchen explaining to mother, in whispers berserk, that I hadn't let myself be messed about.

It is possible to be two things at once, certainly to feel that way, but to be aware of it too. Well, I'm not really too... Certainty pops open, don't you think, like the locket at my chest, and the assurances kept there flutter loose. Gone, again and again, gone. The blood thins and it trickles, tepid between the bones and you're not really too...

I thought, don't think about this, as I thought unavoidably about it. I think it now as I tell it to you.

I can barely believe it. But language conveyed itself from within me; murmurs melted out through the cardigan wool. They did.

'I really do think tact here, would be the best-'

'Of course, tact. Forget tact. For god's sake! They've put her in the cabbage skirt.'

'Well, I'm not really too...'

'Fine. Elixabete!'

My name, too loud.

'Come along then Elixa!'

'Elixabete, really. It would be helpful...'

3.

There were medicines everywhere. I mean vaporised oint-ments, powdered salves, volatile particles all strewn about on the air. Lunchtime light pooled at the windows and I saw the blend swirl thickly over the panes. I imagined plate glass cor-ridors as transparent conduits for all the predictable lunacies.

I needed to see her. I sucked in through my shawl. It's quite simple really, I wanted the doctor to mount an intrusion on my person. Instead the place, the clinic itself, did it on her be-half. Do you understand? She didn't visit, she didn't check in. Occasionally she waved from the courtyard, while the build-ing... well, it was breaking and entering.

I tensed and waited and nothing took place. I did it, not knowing what it was really, and I did it anyway, winced, tensed, waited; I became what I did and all I did was tense, wait. Wait to hear those voices again, to experience their difference again. Idealise a habit and call it ritual. I know all about ritual. Sitting, tensing. Ritual helps you find your way, when it's time to face a change.

I winced, tensed. And sure enough. Voices, from my hips.

'You're volatile Elixa.'

'You are.'

'On a day to day.'

'No results so far. Is that untrue?'

'When one talks to oneself-'

'It's a sensual curiosity. The material-'

'Much harder to ignore. From an observer's perspective, I mean.'

'Tou bi, or not tou bi, contre votre poitrine, it iz ze question?'

'So, volatility...'

'The American girl in Artikutza? At the lake. She said, about swimming, what? Something like, "God, crawl man, it really works your core!" And you, you didn't even know there was a name for it.'

'Now you do. Stand up Elixabete.'

'It's about her body isn't it?'

'It's nothing to do with it! Her appearance is irrelevant. Being seen. We're talking about being seen, dimwit.'

'Enough Ibai! Certainly enough. Enough. Quite enough of that. Up now Elixabete, up and out.'

'Lixa-Lixa, the time-worn wonder, first things first, hands on knees and push. That's it pop right on up to a standing position. Then it's, right, then it's one stick, two stick. Of course, of course you know, you understand.'

'Use the bastard sticks will you, think of your back.'

'Out of bounds is a fascist construct. Age is a fascist construct. This clinic?'

'Likely a fascist construct.'

'Desire. Outweighing desire.'

'This place. It's Farnsworth House, misunderstood. Mies –'

'Shhhhhhhh!'

'Just get to the door and don't let the concierge see you.'

'Try.'

4.

Voices have weight. Of course they do, they occupy space, they carry... and anyway, from their locations, variously around my person, I could infer a shape. A body, my own. They helped to describe it, so I listened and found myself able. To picture what they said. To do as I was told.

The choral voice would come at the end. Until then I had solos, the occasional duet, vocals from the extremities of my person; the marginalised territories urging me to get out, to make a productive mistake.

I leaned into the peninsula, a stick in each hand, stabbing weakly past a clutch of tamarisk trees. I saw the white shine of grey ocean and heard nothing but voices, the language of my body urging me on. I felt something like the thrill of being known. I saw wet boulders, clustered, their bulk sunk deep into tideline pores, as if flicked like marbles by a colossal hand. I stopped and my sticks dangled from my arms as I

111

drew my shawl over my head. I felt something like the thrill of being thrown and I felt my body concur, deeply, as it did the throwing on my behalf.

I was no more than a mile from the clinic when the dim shell, shattered by daybreak, began to mend in delftware plates at the zenith; of course, cobalt specks on the honeyed dusk, walnut lobes of bad weather in the Bay of Biscay. The voices drew close, weaving loose harmonies through my ears. I shuddered and arms rigid, my being drove me on, rubber pucks at the tips of my sticks finding traction in the coastal grit.

It was a harmonics of sentiment. Do you understand? Not melodic. Clustered voices surrounded a beat. Breathing. A particular breath. My old friend Gina Pane. Her breath, as she stomped through a field in Eure. In 1969, her breath, as she walked, it was my fuel, a rhythm we shared. What's more, as I walked, I shared her sky, the sky of Eure in '69, when she buried the sun, laid it to rest, *Enfoncement d'un Rayon de Soleil.*

Slate vapours savaged the coast and of course, there were never going to be illuminations from above. It was hope from within, you do understand? The closest I came to the firmament's glow was the rare blink of peridot and jasper; starboard/port bobbing bulbs on the swell, trailing nets; boats, stalking the would-be bakailao.

My palms burned on the sticks, but the core of my being continued the crawl, continued to shoulder the weight, high up around the headland. Until it didn't. Seized. Each stick clotted in sand and I screamed, nerve branches ripping at the spine. White-out lacerations. The voices rising in unison with the pain – enough! – and I collapsed, slumped against the sticks, sweating, panting as the sky slipped to black.

It rained, of course. Tore through my shawl and the tamarisk bark flayed like rope. Through the distortion, I saw the glass
112

of a bus shelter, rippling. Where was I going, you have asked me. But you understand now, that it is a stupid question. The bus stop was not the destination. I went there nonetheless. There had to be anticipation. And what better place? I rose and made my way dreadfully towards it. Of course I cried. My body moved me; I was moved by it.

I collapsed on the bench. My head toppled against the perspex pane. I sat through the spasms and waited. Something would happen. I winced, I could not tense. I waited for something to happen. I waited for what I knew would come, for what I did not know, but what I knew would come eventually if I winced, could only tense in the appropriate way.

How long had passed? You can probably tell me. There were no timetables, just the beat of my breath. I tried to look through the pane, but a rough commuter had been restless, had cancelled what it offered with the tip of his key. I closed my eyes. Nothing ever changes.

I had hoped for a change. I had tried and it was nearly enough. And on reflection, I should warn you, that in the trying I found the will to try again. I hope you understand what I've said.

Manifesto for Abandoning My Flesh Body and Becoming a Formless Mist

Clouds Haberberg

[Content note: ableism]

The mind inhabits the body the way a tenant inhabits a house – and it is only the mind that can make a body a home.

All body-houses are different, and everyone feels differently about where they live. Sometimes the house is in perfect condition and you're delighted to live there; sometimes it could do with a fresh coat of paint; and sometimes there's black mould on the ceiling, cracks in the walls, you're pretty sure the previous tenant was murdered in the basement, and you can't afford to move.

In disability studies, academics like Margaret Price talk about the concept of the 'bodymind'.[1] They propose that the body and the mind should be treated as a single entity. After all, when one feels pain, it reflects that pain onto the other. When a tenant is sad or under stress, their house gets messy or falls into disrepair, and when a house gets messy or falls into disrepair it causes stress and misery for the tenant.

I'm disabled, and I hate my house. Well, my metaphorical house – my real house is fine. I'm here to propose something radical: let's all move out and go off-grid, by which I mean sublimate ourselves into an aqueous vapour and float in the atmosphere until the inevitable heat death of the universe.

If you still need to be persuaded about this admittedly extreme concept, I've prepared something for you: a manifesto. Maybe, once you've read it, you'll consider joining me.

1. Leisurely

> Mist gathers, then settles. It hovers a while, and – at its own pace – it disperses. It is in no hurry, and has nowhere in particular to be.

1   Margaret Price, 'The BodyMind Problem and the Possibilities of Pain', (*Hypatia*, Volume 30, Issue 1, 2014)

Think of a disabled body as a second-hand car. It might have the same controls as a newer model, and all the same numbers on the speedometer. But it doesn't have all the fancy features: no power steering, no eco-friendly adjustments to the fuel tank, and rubbish suspension. So it goes at half the speed, it needs more frequent refuelling and servicing, it's more expensive to run, and sometimes it'll give up the ghost without warning and leave you stranded on the hard shoulder for hours. This metaphor has its limits – disabled people don't get to trade their body-cars in – but the cost of upgrading components definitely still holds up.

To live in London in 2018 is to live life at 1.5x speed – not so fast as to be unrecognisable, but too fast to be entirely comfortable. Couched in drizzle and smog, it's like inhabiting a low-budget greyscale remake of D.C. Comics' *The Flash* that nobody asked for or wanted. The ancient vehicle that is a disabled body cannot move at the speed the city demands. In mine, I nearly always find myself stranded by the roadside, watching everything and everyone else speed past.

It is no more efficient to travel at speed and stop frequently than to travel slower and keep a constant pace. Where is London trying to go, and why is it so eager to leave disabled people behind?

Forget the TARDIS: if you want to distort the course of time, develop a disability. Gasp as journeys that used to take one hour take three because you have to change trains a million times to find the step-free route. Marvel when your body-car refuses to start because you're too exhausted, anxious, or low on executive function to get moving. It doesn't matter how much time you allocated for the journey; your pace will always be wrong.

I'm very fond of half-seriously labelling abstract concepts as ableist. Here's one: the way we punish lateness is ableist, because in the world we've created – where movement is impossible in an ailing body-car and time is warped by the stress this causes – lateness is inevitable. I can plan until all my pens dry out, but if three bus drivers in a row won't let me on because there is no space for my wheelchair, that's it.

The formless mist moves at its own speed, unburdened by momentum, time constraints, or miscellaneous references to comic books and science fiction. You can't force mist to move at any speed: if the pace is unsustainable, it will disperse and reform elsewhere. Time doesn't govern it the way it does a disabled body.

Join the formless mist. Shed all your concerns about time and pace. You'll never have to worry about people staring at you when you show up late to meetings again.

2. Ageless

Each instance of mist is brand new, but how many times have its water droplets condensed and evaporated? How many bodies has each particle been a part of? Mist is at once as young as a new breath and as old as the world.

My sixty-two-year-old mother refuses painkillers constantly, perhaps as a point of pride. She marches through migraines, sprains, cancer, even, until they bring her to a standstill. On one occasion, she literally walked for three days on a broken ankle. Age has barely slowed her pace: she still works like someone in their twenties, hauls heavy objects around, and is constantly busy.

At thirty, I take painkillers at least twice a day. When I walk, I do so with a cane, like someone more than twice my age. On some days, I can't walk at all, so I use a wheelchair. I have lost count of how many people have told me I'm too young for my mobility aids. As if chronic illness, though pitiless, were nevertheless discerning enough to discriminate based on age; as if I haven't aged fifty years in the span of ten. My flat cap and pipe seem to have got lost in the post, too, so I can't even rock the whole 'old man who likes to shout "get off my lawn"' at teenagers' look. Life is cruel.

Curiously, though, using mobility aids can also reverse aging. It's uncanny – on my feet, I'm 'madam', but in my wheelchair I'm 'poppet' or 'sweetheart' or 'love' – perhaps 'buddy' if my presentation is convincingly masculine enough. In any

117

position, however, I am an adult. In a way, I've beaten the formless mist to break free of physical age: I'm the morning, afternoon and night of the Sphinx's riddle, all at once. More, even – if the Sphinx ever said anything about wheels, it seems to have been lost in translation.

With all this ageing backwards and distortion of timelines, there's probably a remake of *The Tale of Benjamin Button* in here, somewhere. Hit me up, HBO.

Occasionally, my able-bodied friends, or celebrities around my age, will joke about how they can no longer achieve the same feats of endurance or constitution they could in their mid-twenties, and I will nod and try not to cry. The thing about faulty collagen is that – outwardly, at least – it keeps you young. Never mind that I walk at the same pace as my ninety-three-year-old granddad; I get mistaken for an undergraduate every time I set foot in a university. I look years younger than I am, but feel decades older. A body in chronic pain is an ocean of contradictions.

Look at it this way: mist could be every particle ever released by any living thing – every animal's exhalation, every plant's respiration. Mist is anything that's ever evaporated. But it's rejuvenated everywhere, every second, combining with things it's never met before. It truly transcends age, because it's never quite the same thing twice.

Alternatively, look at it this way: mist is made of water. Water doesn't age and isn't subject to humanity's ridiculous ideas about what time means. If it was, it would probably have said 'sod this' and left us all to wither by now.

Join the formless mist. Defy all expectations placed on you by youth or age. You'll never have to answer invasive questions like 'what's a whippersnapper like you doing with a walking stick' again!

3. Beautiful

Mist is an artist in nature, refracting and diffusing sunlight; obscuring the ugliness of the weather, or – in lifting – bestowing clarity. Its shapelessness defines the beauty of

118

its presence.

I am beautiful. It feels so weird to write that. My instinct is to immediately write something self-deprecating to balance it out, but I have a point to make here, so that can wait until later. I might not be 'conventionally attractive', but I'm attractive enough to be privileged. And I am, according to a few self-defined experts on the street – usually male – 'too pretty to be disabled'. Thanks, I guess. I'll be sure to tell my creator that next time we bump into each other at the supermarket.

'I am beautiful.' It looks wrong – both because of how I usually think of myself, and the fact that it no longer feels like it belongs in the plain text of a paragraph in a book. It should be on Instagram or Tumblr with a soft-focus picture of a mountain in the background.

Those words have a weight. They are a political statement. For so many marginalised people – disabled people, people of colour, trans people, fat people – they are seen as a controversial statement. To say them should be freeing, but I'm never sure if it's a weight that I want to carry, whether other people hand it to me or I've picked it up myself.

People who look like me are starting to appear in magazines once in a blue moon, but they're always 'disabled models'. Disability modifies all of my other attributes. Dr Stephen Hawking's achievements were always filtered through the lens of his disability, and so are mine. I'm a disabled writer. A disabled musician. Pretty, for a disabled person. I want to be beautiful, yes – and I am, I am, I am, I'll say it until I feel it – but I don't want to spend my life constructing and defending my own beauty for people who won't look at it. I just want to be.

And I complain, but as an average-sized white person perceived as female, I have an easier time than I would if I was fat, a person of colour, more obviously trans, or any combination of those things. Because fatness is (wrongly) seen as a lifestyle choice, fat disabled people are often blamed for their own illness by both medical professionals and the general public.

The body positivity movement began as an expression of

the beauty of fat bodies. As wonderful and healing as it can be, a lot of its proponents make the mistake of proposing bodily health as some kind of counterbalance to fatness. The aphorism 'look at what this body can do' is cold comfort if your disabilities rule out your ever being able to achieve whichever feat of athleticism it's inevitably captioning on Instagram.

Disabled bodies are beautiful. Their beauty comes from the people inside them, from the non-physical feats they are capable of, from the joy in their hearts. I am beautiful. I have a singing voice that charms everyone who hears it, a written voice that persuades and educates, and a kindness that draws people to me. That and my modesty. So much beauty is erased from the world when people are reduced to their physicality.

Some years ago, during a 5 am journey through the Sicilian countryside, I had the privilege of watching the sun rise over the Hyblaean Mountains. In the shifting hues of the early morning sky I watched the mist rise, unveiling the velvet and ivory of the landscape and bathing it in gold. Mist isn't just beautiful on its own – it reflects beauty onto everything around it. Or, if the 'mysterious and intimidating' aesthetic is more your style, you can take your cues from *The Hound of the Baskervilles* or *Silent Hill*.

Join the formless mist. Isolate your beauty from your shape once and for all. You'll be Instagram-ready anytime, anywhere. #nofilter

4. Fearless

Mist, once evaporated, will condense again elsewhere. It will be changed, yes, in density or character, and transported – but still, it will be. If mist knows anything, it must know that.

Pain and injury are inevitable for anyone, regardless of their body type, but for many disabled people they are as routine as waking up each morning for a job you can't stand. The feeling is almost too pedestrian to be accurately called 'dread', but it's there, gnawing on the corners of the mind like a gerbil in a cardboard tube.

Sometime today, you think, *I will have to make conversation with that wanker from HR whilst we wait for the kettle to boil.*

Lots of offices have That Person who'll loiter silently behind you, waiting for you to surreptitiously check Facebook so they can report you for slacking off. This work environment demands constant vigilance. Is it safe? Are they lingering just out of sight, waiting to catch you out?

Sometime today, I think, *I will shift slightly in my chair, and that tiny movement will nevertheless be enough to dislocate something.*

Just the prospect of leaving the house is fraught with (sometimes imaginary) peril. What if something happens to me whilst I'm out? How will I get home? Will anyone help me? Will anyone notice? Will I be cautioned by the self-appointed Disability Police if I move in a way they think I shouldn't be capable of?

Since disabled people are a workshy bunch of layabouts out for all we can steal – the unmatched wealth of starvation rations and inadequate housing support offered by the UK welfare state – it's only right that we should be pursued by strangers who have no concept of our medical conditions, hurling insults and threats of being reported to the relevant government bodies.

I want to laugh about this. I do. This is where I should be giving you my pithy rejoinder about the internet or age-inappropriate headgear or science fiction, but I'm struggling to find my sense of humour. I constantly look over my shoulder in case someone is monitoring my wheelchair use against the days I walk out of my front door. Every brown envelope that lands on my doorstep gives me a panic attack, regardless of whether it bears the mark of the benefits office.

I use a different name on social media. I try to avoid photos where I'm standing. I try to avoid photos where I'm smiling. In the public imagination, there's no joy for disabled people – only misery and longing. If you challenge that, they'll force fear on you like that colleague who always plays their

121

most obscure, cerebral music on the office stereo in a bid to 'educate' everyone.

There's no real way to threaten mist. Even if it's forced to evaporate, it'll eventually condense somewhere else - different, perhaps, but still there. In any case, water is no more subject to human emotions like fear than it is capable of remembering particles of healing herbs it touched thousands of years ago.

Join the formless mist. Feel no physical pain. Rise, both figuratively and literally, above the busybodies who'd rather see you starve than experience a moment of happiness. You'll never be anxious again. And you'll be water vapour, so you can deactivate the office stereo.

If you feel weighed down by time, age, appearance and fear, the formless mist is beyond feeling or caring, but it is here for you. I'll admit that we don't quite have the science nailed down yet, but if we're working on being able to upload the human consciousness into machines then mists can't be that far behind. The petition will be up on 38 Degrees any day now. Stay tuned.

And if that feels like too much, don't worry. The formless mist understands.

Queer Bodies, Bullseyes
Cara English
[Content note: abortion, homophobia, transphobia]

When they come, depressions descend upon me like clouds; the oppressive Irish rain of my childhood. It's not just that I just can't think, it's that my legs forget how to walk without repeated instruction and my guts refuse to do anything; an apprehensive pressure chamber in constant waiting. The bile builds up and singes my throat, so I take some more pills. An act of fine balancing. Recently I became so anxious I vomited blood, a surprisingly mixed blessing: a horrid physical act but these moments jolt me into reconciling the two mes, that I might live in my head but my head lives in my body. They make me remember that my body exists, probably. A few years of university philosophy have forever tarnished as fallible anything but *cogito ergo sum* – and that it would bode well to look at it every so often. I'll look at it later, I tell myself, I'll take care of it when I have the time, I'll make myself beautiful so men look at me and swoon.

This is what I've been telling myself for three years now, that I will put down the fork and thin happiness will wash over me. When identifying as male, I'd turn my body to serpent and men to putty. I was thin and variously described as 'sexy' and 'scary', both of which worked for me and gave me some of that sweet external evaluation I needed. There was an apathy about who I let engage with this body because I'd decided I was a tenant and didn't really give a shit about the rogue landlord – 'do what you want with this hovel, I'm not getting my deposit back anyway'.

Bodily Revolution
Just owning a body, and recognition of that ownership, is a political act but the problem is that we don't know how radical our body politics should be when magnified from the macro scale to the personal. I want to be a revolutionary, and the sight of me a scourge to sore eyes, but more than that I want to be left alone. My body is for me and for me alone.

It's hard to reconcile these different praxes, but less so when you take into consideration the emotional labour of living in an overweight, masculinised body incongruent with self-image. That's not to say that my gender dysphoria teeters into body dysmorphia, rather that being hosted in a body that is so dissonant with an image of id leads to tightroping several wires: engagements in shops; phone calls with parents; being misgendered by taxi drivers, all the while acutely aware of your physicality sitting in opposition.

Collapsing Categories

Judith Butler deconstructs the essentialism of gendered bodies in her work, writing that rather than a body being gendered, 'the body *becomes* its gender through a series of acts which are renewed, revised, and consolidated through time'.[1] Butler's theory surrounding both the body and gender generally is that categorisation and delineation is fabricated through 'performativity': sex and gender become cross-supporting and reproducing fields of praxis. What that means in the real world is that gender and indeed sex don't exist as realities until we give them the power to do so through attempting to describe them. She goes on to say that as feminists we 'might try to reconceive the gendered body as the legacy of sedimented acts rather than a predetermined [...] fact'. That's not to say that gender does not exist, but that it's the acts or 'performances' of gender to which we ascribe gendered meaning which give life to the concept. Cisgender people are just as guilty as their trans peers of reinforcing and rebirthing gender as a concept through attributing implacable definitions, meanings and alliances to acts. But whilst we can easily recognise the fallacy in reading *acting* empathically, for example, as female-coded, it's more difficult to move away from seemingly verifiable connections, such as 'having a vagina at birth means female'. I won't weaponise the existence of intersex people to counter this any more than I note that nature is a lot more

1   Judith Butler, 'Performative Acts and Gender Constitution: An Essay in Phenomenology and Feminist Theory', (*Theatre Journal*, 1988), Vol 40, No 4, p. 523.

playful and varied than any of us seem to know.

Much as, metaphysically, one cannot move from one gender to another, or from one sex to another, because they are simply categories that live only through virtue of being discussed, reductionist reality doesn't care about lived experiences. We all live gendered and sexed lives, and live in gendered and sexed bodies; it's in the deconstructing, or the creation, of those identities where things become interesting and *real*. One has to go through a series of ticking off checkboxes to be assimilated, or 'unclockable' in a new gender, ticking off the markers of things we see as unquestionably female-making or male-making. As Simone de Beauvoir said, 'one is not born, but becomes a woman', and that seems all too relevant in my current state of transition, where every day I swallow a pill to block further testosterone production. The irony of the pill being blue is not lost on me. Sticking on a new patch of estrogen, prescribed by a ludicrously unaffordable private GP by virtue of an NHS unprepared for an explosion in trans people, I can only think of those for whom this isn't an option. Access to necessary medication, or more accurately, access to the money needed to get these medications, can mean the difference between life and death for many trans people.

Gender Absolutism

Without getting too 'Introduction to Gender Studies', capitalism can exist only under the framework of binary genders being tightly regulated and their rules regurgitated through the same experiences being lived again and again. That's not to say that divergent bodies will immediately bring about whatever comes after neoliberalism, but the wider acknowledgement of our existence at least shines a light on the dark, doomed days of late stage capitalism. The binary nature of the popular imagining of biological sex makes for easy categorisation of what roles we all must play under patriarchy: women as caregiver, men as hunter (or the postmodern translation of that, the city bro). These schisms are so important in keeping society running, business as usual, that any divergence from them is struck down with fevered ridicule or violence often culminating in murder, mental or physical. Trans and non-binary people often wish to have no part in the patriarchal iteration of gender, but do not exist in a vacuum absent of society and its dictatorial rules of engagement. Sometimes we're forced to adapt: to feign telephone voices for an unseen caller, to use 'she' instead of 'they', to resign yourself to using the men's toilet because it's a make-up-free day and you'll be read as male in the women's loos and threatened with arrest.

As Julia Serano says about trans people, 'because we are a threat to the categories that enable traditional and oppositional sexism, the images and experiences of trans people are presented in the media in a way that reaffirms, rather than challenges, gender stereotypes'.[2] The very possibility of 'transitioning', of moving between genders, challenges the reification of modern and capitalist categories of sex and thus sexism. The transgendered body stands reviled as totemic of the possibility of change.

For me, this change is taking the form of a physical sloughing. Once or twice a week I will have a heated needle shoved into hundreds of hair follicles on my face to attain the ultimate in feminine passing – smoothness. When I was still questioning my gender and unsure of where the whole thing might take me, I announced quite innocently to a friend that I was going to be a bearded lady. I think at the time I genuinely meant it: in a bizarre twist, I'd become as attached to my facial hair as it had to me. It wedded me to a solid concept of my expected gender, comforting if incongruent. I'd longed for facial hair as a child, hoping it would quell the internal dissonance by assuring me that I was indeed a burly and unquestionable man.

But with a solidifying of a transfeminine identity came the desire to conform to patriarchal ideals of female beauty, thus the acquisition of a dewy, hair-free face was item number one in my Trans Starter Pack.

2   Julia Serano, *Whipping Girl: A Transsexual Woman on Sexism and the Scapegoating of Femininity* (London: Hachette, 2007), p. 36.

Shape Policing

It's difficult, but not impossible, to reconcile the fact of finding the beauty standards imposed upon women arcane and dictatorial with the desire to adhere to them, if even flimsily. As stated before, trans people cannot be held as being more culpable of upholding cultural beauty standards to importance than their cisgender cohort. What makes this particularly pertinent is the frequent duality of the lived experience of gender dysphoria with the very real pressure to conform to the beauty standards of our 'acquired gender' that we're even more unlikely than our cisgender peers to ever be able to achieve or adhere to. I often place myself in an abeyant state, seen as guilty of both upholding and reinforcing expectations of gendered beauty, whilst simultaneously and systematically eradicating them by my very existence as a non-passing trans woman. I look and am implacably trans - any physical changes to my body will be slow, almost undetectable from the outside, but transitioning isn't a process of receiving external evaluation. I get the evaluation anyway: a double-edged sword of either seeming to appropriate femininity for the sake of ingratiation, or of being seen as not doing enough, not changing enough, to be read as woman. *There's no way of winning.*

Stranger Interactions

When strangers call me 'sir', it may fill me with a resonant dread, but it's ultimately harmless. If the conversation continues and if I think it necessary to tell them that I am indeed a woman, there's mostly no questioning on their part. There's often a clipped 'oh sorry for misgendering you' but rarely a looking up-and-down, or a search for minutiae they can add to their arsenal. It seems Joe, Jane and Jamie Bloggs are already thinking one step ahead of the binaried expectations of what we as trans people should look like. Mostly, they don't care and that is liberation.

Laurie Penny says that 'one's biological sex' should not have to dictate 'anything about one's behaviour, appearance, or the eventual layout of one's genitals and secondary sex or-

127

gans', this being 'the radical heart of feminist thought'.[3] The end goal of all feminisms must be complete and indisputable bodily autonomy for every person, achievable only through a loosening of sexed strictures and their supposedly self-evident boundaries. I'm using all the tools at my disposal to forge corporal arcadia in myself: if I'm svelte, my cheekbones rounded and my lips plumped, men in pubs will look on, confused and horny, and I will pity their atavism. If our feminism is going to be radical (and not trans-exclusionary radical) and intersectional, it has to not only take into account the real possibility of bodily variance, but also recognise capitalism's role in facilitating the creation of new, radical forms of bodies hitherto unseen. If feels like we're killing the goose and taking the golden eggs for ourselves.

Queer Bodies, Bullseyes

When Tom Daley announced he and his husband were expecting a child, a brazenly homophobic backlash waged a meek battle against common sense. Why was the woman in this equation being erased – was the future of queer liberation to be the dissolving of a woman's role in childbearing? What the non-story looked like from the outside was more: two, non-trans people denied any semblance of parenthood – for what, so a woman could take her rightful role as womb-in-chief? Transversely, this discourse centred the woman in question as a vessel-carrier, stripped of her agency in deciding not to make a show horse of herself as surrogate, but rather in using her body with agency as an actualised tool under capitalism. There are rightful conversations to be had about the role of people with wombs under capitalism (forced to bear children of rape in Ireland, unable to access lawful, unrestricted abortion in over 60 per cent of the world) but the supposed erasure of this surrogate was simply a bad faith argument against a queer couple's right to family life. Whatever your views of equal marriage (assimilationist parroting of heteronormative values, or milestone on path to queer lib-

3   Laurie Penny, *Meat Market: Female Flesh Under Capitalism* (London: John Hunt Publishing, 2010), p. 45.

eration), the bondages that women's bodies have been victim to mustn't be weaponised.

Arguments made by those who seek to denigrate trans people only work to undermine themselves. Not standing up to logistic integrity, they stand to reason that women must be centred in the biologically essentialist and reductionist act of childbearing. In doing so, they only highlight how patriarchal and capitalist concepts of what a family must look like are self-reinforcing. The gendered body is brought back to its essence: doer and done-upon, male and female, subject and object. It would be easy to openly debunk these essentialist arguments, but who am I to stage a sexual coup on a trans man's pregnant belly, or use the physical realities of intersex people's bodies to dissect a binary notion of sex?

When my non-trans cousin announced she was having a baby with her wife, the question on everyone's lips was not whose sperm it was (or why the father was being erased), but rather which of them would have the joyous role of host. The sperm-giver was mysteriously absolved of any involvement because we had not just one but two women on which to lavish magnanimity. We take a particular and peculiar ownership over all women's bodies – they exist for reproduction under consumption, so it seems only right that the mega-tribe takes a misogynistic interest in collective concubinage.

Much like homophobia, transphobia's roots lie in an orderly building and rebuilding of normality. What purpose can a person have if they can't have a child? This kind of unquestioned reproduction reproduces hierarchy for hierarchy's sake. There's an inherent terror of trans people such as myself who, deigning to take (possibly) infertility-causing hormone replacement therapy, reject our bodies as forces of creation for anything other than themselves. My body will change shape in the many ways I deem right for myself. However, there remain few things as reviled as the trans woman: emancipation through complete and absolute bodily autonomy despite the collective claim to shape policing, refusal of reduction to sexed site of reproduction, and, worst of all, shifting to such a shameful and reviled body as that of a woman.

129

Governmental Demands on Bodily Autonomy

Notwithstanding an emerging undercurrent of transphobia to take the place of decades of open homophobic rhetoric, things are somewhat improving for gender diverse people. The governments of several countries have decided that perhaps switching from an f to an m on a slip of paper isn't something they should expend so much energy on, and have begun removing barriers. Some have even gone as far as allowing their citizens to identity outside the binary, and permit X markers on official documents.

The framework in the UK is one of medicalised testimony to an actual Gender Recognition Panel, to whom you have to prove your 'new identity' as though gender is something that can be proven outside of bureaucratic demands (e.g. proof of having lived in 'an acquired gender' for several years; being diagnosed with gender dysphoria). Forced sterilisation is still a reality for trans people who wish to change their legal gender across a lot of the world, even in the ersatz home of human dignity that is Europe. I don't want children, but the state taking away my ability to do so so that it can change my gender marker on documents seems just a bit too much.

The government has heeded calls for a system of self-determination of gender identity in line with international best practice, with Theresa May having positioned herself as an unexpected figurehead in the ongoing fight for trans equality. Daily I encounter people online trying to 'enter into a discussion' about self-determination, by which I mean transphobes baring their teeth to the reality that allowing people to put words to who they are won't erase womanhood. I have already been able to change my name, driving license and passport with a simple statutory declaration, so it seems illogical to gatekeep what amounts to the changing of a number at HMRC and the NHS.

In a sort of Orwellian wet dream, homonationalism has taken hold of the UK's political parties, as they continue their courtship with queer and gender diverse people across the country. This makes for messy red lines and discourse: yes, the UK's political administration may be an increasingly reactionary and populism-pandering meshwork, but its paternalistic rhetoric is marketable as radically advancing a queer agenda. How can they possibly be the bad guys if they're the ones advocating for greater queer autonomy? That must mean they're our defenders, then, and the oppressors are the immigrants whose beliefs don't automatically chime with ours, right? This is how the machine is built to work, but we cannot allow ourselves to be cogs in it – successive governments creating and reinforcing a polarised enmity between queer people and those seeking the land of milk and honey cannot be allowed to define the hivemind.

Governments should not and cannot dictate what shapes our bodies take, or must take in order to access certain spaces. It makes sense for the government to make tentative statements, then sit back and let their words cannibalise themselves. Creating policies that respect human dignity seems like slog – much easier for the populace to spar it out, let a consensus be reached by the winner, then the government can claim authorship of whatever has been decided by those with the strongest lungs. Meanwhile, trans people, myself included, are openly attacked in public spaces for simply existing.

With all of this happening, transphobic missives are reeled off in fascist mouthpieces with no possibility of the recourse of engagement for those of us with bodies which cannot or will not be easily confined to the binary categorisation of our genitals at birth. What this fails to reflect is that our bodies aren't going to stop reflecting the diversities of the natural kingdoms, or that freedom to explore gender diversity in all its bounty can only lead to wider liberation through bodily autonomy. Trans, non-binary and gender diverse people have always existed and will always exist: my only hope is that we can exist freely, where our experiences are valued and our voices listened to, where perceptions of our beauty and character are as wide as for everyone else.

Bullies of America
Livia Franchini

Hero

As a young girl, I fancied ex-child actors.

> *His own body moves a step closer, then another, and his hands on the gun are practised, steady, and in that steadiness I can see the appeal of him for the first time.*[1]

Who are your heroes? is the sort of question the hero asks in a movie. Sometimes the hero asks the question openly; more often it is implied in his behaviour. Sometimes, the question is asked out loud by a narrator, a disembodied voice that begins to tell the story from the start, already knowing how it ends. In that case, it is frequently revealed that the narrator's hero is his best friend, whom the narrator has been looking up to his whole life. Often, the narrator is a writer, which justifies his willingness to be telling the story. Often the occasion for the telling of the story is that his friend is recently deceased, possibly from a violent death, which may or may not have taken place at the same time as he was carrying out heroic actions, proving to be a good man. Sometimes the two men – the hero and the writer – have become estranged over time, in which case the story is told in a flashback to their early teenage years. These childhood friendships are often desperate affairs, symbiotic relationships in which the two boys only have each other to count on, their families having disappeared or disintegrated due to tragedy, illness or addiction. Together the two boys develop a shared moral compass, which carries them into adulthood. Despite this, more often than not, having successfully turned into men, their paths diverge.

The fact of the hero – the fact of the hero coming into existence – is the very reason why the movie is being made.

1   Sophie Mackintosh, *The Water Cure*, (London: Penguin, 2018), p. 237.

The hero *is* the story. *Who are your heroes?* For the movie to work, an answer to the question must be withheld until we reach the end of the film, when we can finally confidently agree: *that's him.* He's the one. We realise, as we exit the cinema, that we probably could've guessed it by the size of his name on the poster.

Some general remarks upon the hero:

The hero excels at several things – one of which is obviously sports, although he doesn't always elect to play on a school team.

The hero offers excellent advice to his friends.

The hero will always step in to break up a fight between strangers.

The hero's chosen profession is lawyer, journalist, researcher of current affairs: this is due to the hero's compulsion to tell the truth.

The hero is fiercely loyal to family. He is generally attached to his original family, despite there often being several complex relationships at play within the familial nucleus, meaning the hero must learn to negotiate the human complexity of adults from an extremely early age. Though this difficult task proves ultimately beneficial towards character-building, the hero is subject to vocally expressing an urge not to become 'like his father'. Meaning that when the hero will finally move onto a target family he will act as an optimum patriarch – a great Dad – which is the act of final redemption of the hero, and his heritage. It is a generous concession of power to his offspring, from which generations to follow will benefit. As the hero relinquishes masculine aggressivity to turn into an affectionate father, he is cleansed of the sins of masculinity. The hero is a generational marker: the first to stay out of jail. Finish school. Go to university. Get killed in a brawl to save a random man from being bottled in a bar.

The hero represents masculine freedom and social mobility.

The bullies crouch in their leather jackets, holding
onto each other's arm

outside them is a larger circle of vehicles
released, 2 fighting cockerels enter the ring of compact dust

However: if the hero dies in the beginning of the movie,
and the narrator lives on to tell the story, is it possible that
there are really two heroes? The hero that relates the truth to
us and the hero whose truth we relate to. Given the fact that
the hero must die for the story to even begin to unfold, would
we wish to stick around, like the writer? What if the writer
is a woman? What is the hero is a heroine? Could you, then,
relate to her?

Strongboy

The boys in the woods stand guard
their fathers having disappeared in the war
come back crazy from the war

> *The familiar territory of men, boys and their
> fathers.*[2]

Who are your heroes? You must pick ones that are
appropriate to you, and the place where you grew up, its
possibilities: heroes you can feasibly approximate – even
when 'approximate' might only stretch to the meaning of
'living in proximity of'. When living in the provinces, it is
always a safer bet to pick a local hero as an icon: narrowing
the distance will minimise the magnitude of a possible failure
to match up.

> *When I was thirteen I wanted a punching bag
> and boxing gloves for my birthday [...] these ac-
> coutrement of masculine competition [...] signi-*

2   Judith Halberstam, *Female Masculinity* (Durham, NC: Duke
University Press, 1998) p. 18.

fied for me a way [...][3]

My maternal grandfather dies and shortly after this happens I hear my mother refer to herself casually in conversation as her father's male son. My paternal grandmother, who has a complicated relationship with my mother, has vocally observed several times that my mother and her sisters were raised like boys. My paternal grandfather was known to rebuke my father for having 'girly' hands, meaning that he was no good at practical tasks. It is unclear to me if my grandfather's rebuttal was triggered by my father's lack of ability at manual work, or rather, having come unprompted, caused my father to never attempt DIY (not even later in life). It is also possible, of course, that my father was never interested in DIY at all, to which he seems to me perfectly entitled. My father and I look very alike, uncannily so when it comes to our hands, which are exactly the same size, although his are small for a man's; mine, large for a woman's.

At the age of six, in the kitchen, I coil a lock of my hair around my father's index finger and begin to spin on the spot, braiding the hair tighter and tighter around his finger. My scalp does not hurt, but after a while it does feel numb. 'You've got such strong hair,' says my father. He calls my mother over, 'Look at this!' he tells her. 'She's got such strong hair.' I am brown–skinned and straight as a rod, with hair as strong as a rope: I am a beautiful child. At twelve my body lets me down by turning itself, seemingly overnight, into the body of a woman. I don't know what to do with it. I am terrible at running and suffer a minor public humiliation during a mildly competitive athletics session. My father takes me out to the council's football pitch in the morning to teach me, so it won't happen again. As I run in circles through the overgrown grass he kindly reminds me to keep my elbows closer to my sides. Shortly after this, I chop all of my hair off, very short. In the photographs I look so uncomfortable it makes it hard for me to see, even now.

3   Judith Halberstam, *Female Masculinity* (Durham, NC: Duke University Press, 1998)., p. 267.

The boys' chest has a dent in the middle
a higher transparency between the chest and the
heart
everywhere else there is puppy fat

One of the earliest memories I have is of a joke that my mother and I share each morning when I am about two, while she is getting me ready for playschool. First, she strips me out of my pyjamas. I stand in my pants on the bed. My mother says, 'Now be a hunk' and I stick my tiny chest out, curl up my tiny biceps, and parade up and down the mattress.

My mother also tells me this story: when she is twelve, maybe thirteen, she goes to a party thrown by older friends – friends of her sister, who is five years older. She is wearing a trouser suit that she likes very much. There are boys. After a while, one approaches her. My mother cannot believe she is being noticed – not even that: to be seen at all when she is so much younger than him, feels like a big enough blessing. The boy blows her fringe out of her face (or so I imagine). He slides a finger around the cup of her ear, gently pushing back her hair. 'Is this an ear or a fried chicken steak?' he asks.

The Body

> "Lost years. Gained ideals. Not yet developed. Much past the time in which our pubes fail to grow." In gym class he would dress in a bathroom stall rather than open himself up to the inspection of the boys' locker room.[4]

The bullies play games of baseball with the mailboxes
they polish metal parts that belong to the engine
they carve the initials of the gang name into each
other's arm

4   Charles R. Cross, *Heavier than Heaven,* (London: Sceptre, 2001), p. 51.

As for my imagination, back then it is the same as any other girl's from a southern European country. The metal mailboxes of American suburbia align with the trees on the lined stretch of state road that leads from the town to the seaside. It takes twenty minutes to get from A to B, if you drive fast enough, so it isn't exactly a highway, but at this point we have only left our town a countable number of times, fewer still with only our friends. A trip to the beach still feels like a big deal. Where the road leans abruptly to the right – the suicide bend, about halfway down – stands a small red brick house. It's falling apart: its crumbling sides covered in graffiti, a single paneless window. The front is lined with flower offerings, their plastic wrappings covered in mud. I think, if this were America, I imagine this is where the bullies would meet. I imagine they'd park their motorbikes behind the shed.

> *I was twelve-going-on-thirteen the first time*
> *I saw a dead human being. It happened in the*
> *summer of 1959, a long time ago – but only if*
> *you measure it in terms of years.*[5]

In the mythology of adolescence the first boy to die a violent death in one's school becomes a hero, of sorts. The boy who dies when I am a girl, G, carries the name of a famous British singer, though he is not British and the singer he has been named after belongs to a generation we don't know much about, and so perhaps it is only coincidence that they share the same name. The Fiat Ritmo attempts a fast overtake on that stretch of the road where it bends to the right, only it carries on as normal, in a straight line, into a tree trunk. Strike 1.

Of the four that die (there were five in the car) G is the oldest, the most handsome. He is the one everyone remembers. His odd consonant-ending name resurfaces from time to time, hieratic, carved into the wooden spine of bar furniture. G and the boys who died in the car crash. After all these years, still boys, written on benches in girls' handwriting. After the

[5]   Rob Reiner (Dir.), *Stand by Me*, (1986).

accident we learn that G had kissed one of our friends on the mouth the night before he died. After a few days we find out through the inconsistencies in their stories that he'd actually kissed several girls. Each of them thought she was his girlfriend. These girls – our friends – are unsure of what to do with regards to mourning him. When one takes the plunge and makes a trip to the mortuary, the other ones follow suit, though in separate instalments. Paying a visit to G's dead body quickly becomes a duty, a mark of authenticity: a bar has been raised, and this has now become the correct way to grieve him as grown-ups, which is all we desperately want to be at this point, and especially so during a time of crisis. This time the details of the girls' stories all match: his body is unrecognisable. 'It really hits home,' says one girl. 'It's hard to believe it's the real him,' says another. We understand only then how very alive he had been before: kissing a girl in the schoolyard, then her best friend round the back of the gym. We learn to forgive boys early, the hard way.

> As he left, Courtney and Mason were brought into the viewing room. Kurt was on a table, dressed in his nicest clothes, but his eyes had been sewn shut. It was the first time Courtney had been with her husband for ten days, and it was the last time their physical bodies would be together. She stroked his face, spoke to him and clipped a lock of his hair. Then she pulled his pants down and cut a small lock of his pubic hair – his beloved pubes, the hair he had waited so long for as an adolescent, somehow needed to be preserved.[6]

Nobody makes a film about G, but then again here I am, writing about him. Nobody talks about the girl who died in the car next to him, and even I don't remember very much about her, except for the fact that we all knew she had been

6   Charles R. Cross, *Heavier than Heaven*, (London: Sceptre, 2001) p. 50.

there but never spoke about it. She didn't match the story in our heads, so we simply ignored her.

Princess Peach

> *Female adolescence represents the crisis of the coming of age as a girl in a male-dominated society. If adolescence for boys represents a rite of passage of social power, for girls, adolescence is a lesson in restraint, punishment and repression.*[7]

Eventually, I grow my hair back. I get used, best as I can, to my own new body. In the final year of high school I become friends with A, who has long brown hair down to her belt. Each morning she brushes her hair for a long time, then tidies it into a braid – loosely, so as not to sacrifice precious centimetres of length to her choice of hairstyle. At our school, long hair is a mark of success: both the straight girls and the alt girls wear the same kind of hairstyle, which is, really, no style at all, just loose, long hair, as long as possible. The soft end of A's hair swipes gracefully at her waist when she moves, like a natural animal tail. One day, A and I fall out, although I am not sure exactly what happened, or why it has. I find out that she is angry with me from mutual friends; right after they confess this to me, she makes different friends. Though she is the one who has decided to end it, she says she cannot help but mourn the death of our friendship. She sends me a letter through the post. 'I thought we could be beautiful together,' she writes, 'In different ways, beautifully different. But it doesn't seem to be enough for you.' She is right: it isn't enough. Because she has to specify 'different', when all I want is to erase difference, to be exactly the same as her. When the letter comes, I realise our friendship has ended because of a terrible misunderstanding on her part. She has miscast me as

7   Judith Halberstam, *Female Masculinity,* (Durham, NC: Duke University Press, 1998), p. 267.

an equal: I hadn't conceived of our friendship on a level so I hadn't considered I could make her feel threatened. I had looked up to A as my hero. She knew how to be a girl and I admired her for that.

> When I was thirteen I wanted a punching bag and boxing gloves for my birthday, I believe these accoutrement of masculine competition signified for me a way to keep adult womanhood at bay [...]
>
> When I was a teenage girl no explanation needed to be given for the narrowing of a girl's life once she'd hit puberty; indeed adolescence produced a logic all of its own, and all challenges to that logic were simply more evidence of one's irrational attachment to inappropriate behaviour. Adolescent girls, according to such logic, must manage their bodies in such a way as to optimize their appearance, to appeal to boys, stave off rape and sex and display appropriate levels of [...][8]

Occasionally, I think of A when the women who I am friends with tell me that they can't come out that evening because they plan to wash their hair. Once I think about A at my friend E's family home, where I have gone to visit her for her birthday. E introduces me to another friend who never dries her long, blonde hair after a shower, putting it up in a tight, damp coil at the top of her head. There is snow outside, it is the coldest winter I have ever known. In school, quite a few of my girlfriends claim to have 'sensitive hair'. In Italian they say, *soffro di capelli*, which literally translates into 'I suffer with hair'.

My hair is still numb. I still miss A, sometimes; I still feel bad.

8   Judith Halberstam, *Female Masculinity* (Durham, NC: Duke University Press, 1998), p. 267.

Marilyn

*At our show opening for Jon Spencer Blues
Explosion at La Luna in Portland, I grew
agitated at their crowd's indifference toward
us and kicked the microphone stand into the
audience. Jon voiced his dissatisfaction at my
puerile behaviour, more aware than I was that
there is a difference between conjuring a sense
of danger and actually harming someone. But
I wanted our shows not to just be galvanic, I
wanted to destroy the room. More than that,
I wanted to obliterate myself, to unlock and
uncork the anger, to disappear into the sound
and into the music. When I kicked my legs out
toward the crowd or swung my guitar close to
the heads in the front row, it was about trying
to physically harness the moment, to crash into
strangers in a horrible but ecstatic impact, a
shared bruising.*[9]

I keep a tab open on my browser for an article titled
'World's Oldest Man Says Petty Grievances Keep Him Going.'
Women of course tend to outlive men in age and I, for one, am
constantly caught up in anger.

I begin to play guitar in a punk band when I think I am
too old to begin playing at all. Before then, I have never
felt capable of playing music in public, though somewhat
puzzlingly, since I have much experience in the field, having
owned a guitar since I was thirteen, having endlessly facilitated
male musicians for the last fifteen years. I have carried kit for
my male friends, ghostwritten their songs, hooked them up
with other male musicians, run their shows, brought them
beers, provided them with ideas that they could plagiarise in
their mediocre radio singles: a variety of tasks for which the
word 'groupie' is usually employed as shorthand. When I first

9   Carrie Brownstein, *Hunger Makes Me A Modern Girl* (London:
Virago Press, 2015), pp. 162-163

join a band I am part of a loving community of women, and it is their encouragement that enables me to begin playing in the first place. For a while, the effort of using my body in a completely new way makes me forget that I'm not very good at what I am doing: it is a joyful few months, a great time of making. As soon as I become better at it, the anger is back. I am excited about the anger at first, I invite it in: I have an outlet now, I'm thinking, I can turn it into sound. The settings on my pedal chain allow for more room for my anger to unfold: I fiddle with them endlessly, striving to find the perfect combination. I want my guitar to sound like a drill, a saw, a truck unloading a load of rocks onto a concrete floor. It's never enough to help in the long run. The more I learn, the more I find things that bother me, though I have only been playing guitar for a matter of months, and I am slowly but steadily improving with practice. I have intrusive thoughts about the kind of comments that I know a boy would make, watching me play: that I have bad wrist technique in my right hand and even worse picking, that I don't know anything about intervals. My anger is trapped within the boundaries of my body, it stops, choked up, at my strumming hand.

Do you sing? asks an ex I don't speak to very often, when I tell him I have joined a band. I say no. *Do you write lyrics?* I say no: I play the guitar. *Don't your breasts get in the way of the strap?* He wants to know how I wear it: to the right side, to the left side, between them? At live shows I face my amp to hide my hands, make sure that no one laughs at my guitar face.

The bullies have guns
they are careless with them
they leave them around for their little brothers to see

Quickly, I develop a bad pain in my right shoulder and this is because when I play I'm all tensed-up: I am conscious of my body in irreversible ways, too old and afraid to afford a real bruising. I'm all coiled up like a guitar pick-up, though this doesn't help with playing. I've taken care to insulate my

143

ego with protective swathes of irony, and though I know this is wrong – a kind of acting – at worst disrespectful of others, I realise I will never be able to strip all the layers back. I become frustrated with my inability to play objectively difficult patterns: I don't give up, or give myself time, but I overthink them, making it even worse. I will never air-guitar with intention, which I must stupidly, subconsciously grieve, because of how I inflict myself on the women around me when I feel this way. I act like a perfectionist about something I am not even fully equipped to do. Playing guitar then, becomes as frustrating as writing. I remind myself that Virginia Woolf said you never produce your best work when you are angry. When I remember that, I also remember that I was never sure whether I believed or agreed with her when I first read it.

> [...] the music I make has really helped me figure out my own feminism, my own privilege and probably actually helped me stop totally disassociating from my own body.[10]

Adulthood comes with heartbreak or the full realisation of my unresolved relationship with my own female body – a deep-set acceptance that I am not likely to ever feel at home in it. In my life I look the most like a girl when I am at my least happy. Femininity is a cancellation: a concealment of my body when I can no longer recognise it – myself – as mine. A giving up, giving into the round edges of the body: here they are, I relinquish control over these boundaries, let them grow, because attempting to stop the process is too tiresome and it becomes more tiresome with age. Once I have handed my body over to the mere, biological notion of gender, I am no longer responsible for it. For a few months, while heavily depressed, I get manicures. I also often get blackout drunk. Around this time, two close female friends refer to me as 'sort of a Marilyn', which is obviously meant to cheer me up, but that I immediately perceive to mean ridiculous, clumsy, dis-

10   Katy Cotterell in *Move Under Your Own Power*, ed. Kirsty Fife, p. 10.

tracted, a caricatural woman, out of a need to distance myself from the uncomfortably soft, bodily implications of the comparison. 'You should take a fucking compliment sometimes,' I tell myself, seeking refuge in a more comfortable, familiar type of self-loathing. I don't. Around the same time, while on a trip back to my hometown, I meet a male acquaintance of mine, whom I want to impress because I admire his sharp wit. He acts warmly towards me, commenting on the carefree attitude that I am trying so hard to project. It is a hot summer evening, and I am wearing no tights. I am drunk.

'I envy you,' he says, 'Look at you. All you have to do is pop a nice dress on.'

In the woods the boys keep up their morale
they haven't washed for days
in the bushes they wait in hiding

Another Evening Swim

Rosie Haward

It was a bright day – hovering between the leftover chill of winter and the warmth of March sun. A few of us were wearing thin shirts with no sweaters, the heat in the room rising as it filled with bodies and gentle laughter. It seemed an appropriate afternoon to celebrate a birthday – the breeze outside was calmer than was usual on this stretch of coast and the sun was sparkling on the glassy sea outside the large front windows.

Sounds bounced up to the ceiling, then returned to the room. From where she was sitting in the corner she could probably hear fragments of conversations and high laughter, perhaps the clinking of a glass. A thick grey strand of hair fell into her face. I wasn't that interested in her anymore, but still couldn't look for long at the wisps of hair at the nape of her neck, catching a familiar tilt of the head or intonation of a word if I did. Tangled strands and buttery tones fluttered through me.

Neglected blobs of dried paint bumped under the surface of her fingers as she ran them over the fresh gloss, startling in the spring sun that fell in shafts into the room. She struggled to her feet, placing a hand to steady herself as her heel scraped the floor, a flake of paint clinging to its curve, not falling away as I'd expected.

When I entered the room it was airless and tightly wound. I felt compressed by the eyes that fell on me, my presence having been met with cries of welcome that moved from a seemingly muffled distance to a bright proximity. The day seemed in sharp relief to those which preceded it; a strange treat to be free-floating for hours in one room. Provided for. A slow, seductive shift from daily life that describes so many moments of occasion, tied up as they are with expectation.

I was so drunk that I sometimes wonder if this night wasn't actually another; she pulled up my worn grubby t-shirt and bit and sucked my breast. I left to throw up. Returned, head heavy and lashes damp as I stumbled past. Not looking at her.

My trousers hugged my hips and stomach, flaring out from my thighs. If I took off my shoes the hems would pool around my feet. I tried to look at ease, but kept rolling my sleeves down every time the clouds obscured the light I was standing in, then back up when it returned. The touch of warm light on my back was reassuring, and eased me into the lull of alcohol. For the first hour I was content and distracted by turns.

I smashed a glass and leant straight onto it. Fucking stupid. It didn't rip my shirt but sliced a nice two-inch-long cut along my forearm, and blood was seeping through my sleeve. I remembered finding her first grey hair – thick and wiry – and she laughed when I said it was sexy. Her stray hairs stayed on my bedside table. I didn't quite have the guts to keep them anywhere safe, but consciously enjoyed finding them on my jumpers, taking my time to unravel them from the knit, savouring their length and the reddish tint they had when they caught the light.

I missed it all. Your room full of smoke, and me thick in sleep. The beach is close, the beach I tripped along, and you are over there.

In the months between her and now, guys had tried it on, laid me down on the stones and slipped their hands up my skirt. I made it easy. 'Let's swim!' Cold, and quickly bored, drifting up and over their heads into the familiar tree-tops opposite. Letting myself slip into almost giving positions. Flirting eyes but distant hands that couldn't be convinced. I saw lush grass; tickling blades and the smell of stomach-swooping spring. I wish she'd sung to me. She probably never sings, even to herself. But yes, the grass. I've weighed down the ground with feet and hands and head. Hairs left behind, drinks spilt and crocodile tears. I've watched friends flirt and been jealous but revolted. Thinking of when I'd put a hand on her leg in the pub, just to try it. Then she'd put hers on top of mine and it meant our arms sliced through the space inside the circle of chairs, people looking over, I think. Soon she was folding my

148

clothes up as I slept and placing them on her desk chair, my damp knickers on top of her synthetic tops. On top of, on the top of.

Stop looking at him.

The building was expensive with high ceilings. With its many sealed doors it held rooms unknown to even its most frequent of visitors. Rooms waiting for bodies to occupy them, longing for the caress of a hand. The painted wood floor probably moved under the doors and continued, spreading itself into unknown corners, enhancing the echo-y quality that permeated the central space, no soft fabrics to absorb the noise of voices. I tried a couple of doors, wanting momentary quiet.

Her clothes were too tight, and I knew the waist belt she'd donned would sit oddly on her straight sides. High-up skirt bunched in and restricting her legs. Smooth and clean-looking. Similarly dressed women surrounded her, not seeing her fingers as they wrapped around a sticky looking glass, a thin layer of fizz sliding around the bottom. The liquid just about making it to the rim before she abruptly lifted it up to rest in the crook of her elbow, crossing her arms. One hip pushed to the side, ankles crossed and then uncrossing before she moved into the only windowless room. Flickering pinky light briefly spilling out of the door as she stepped through.

The lights bathing her head in colour, for a second.

The dancing we did was slow and intense. Simultaneously much too aware and much too unaware of those around us. Not really friends.

The first time we met I pushed you into the bathroom with me. Did you like it? We were laughing and you tried to stop me in case we were heard. Somehow it seemed like the best place to be, not illicit but opportune. I was the queen of the opportune.

149

Billowing pillows of grey curtain momentarily filled pockets of space in the room. One particularly fierce gust of wind made the fabric brush my elbow. I can't tell whether it was the cool of the air or the touch that gave me goosebumps. Suddenly chilled and looking at the blue-painted walls I wondered why anyone would pick that colour.

If I paid enough attention then I could see the patterns made by the guests as they circled, almost gracefully, around the room. Shuffling to the left, then almost always moving in an anti-clockwise direction. I don't know whether this was because the curve of the right-hand wall seemed an inviting space to stand, or because the drinks table was at the jutting end of this wall, but it meant that I could watch small queues of legs forming against the sweep of shell-pink plaster. These legs would relax into wobbly circles, their backs leaning and glasses congregating at the centre of their torsos.

The breathy voice of the singer spread through the room and the chatter momentarily abated.

Her birthdays were usually uncomfortable. I was too enthusiastic, trying to return a level of care and generosity she set for herself but seemed so embarrassed of when it came from me. My presents turned into unfathomable objects that came to represent an excess of care, when she'd rather be left alone. Whenever I saw those gifts in her room they were in relief from the space around them, surfaces prominent because she hadn't chosen them. They were objects that were of me, and so wouldn't settle. Drawing my attention as if vibrating in the hostile atmosphere.

This year we'd spent the day with our feet dangling in the lake. It wasn't so warm that I wanted to pull off my clothes, but warm enough to sit with our feet submerged. Mine wobbling to and fro next to hers, which appeared even longer and paler than usual.

Quivering sun, weak in southern England but a place I can brave it. I want to. Your skin wasn't quite porcelain – not that special – but compressed powder, easily disturbed.
150

You should have stayed in the womb; you were invaded by the bite of rain drops, witchy and wanting to melt. But you were still able to seduce me in the shower later, water in my open mouth and spilling down my chin. Movie star. When I'd asked you if you wanted to swim you looked at me as if I was trying to seduce you. This look was very similar to the one you had when I knew you wanted to fuck me. Watching you sink into the lapping green I wondered what you felt. I'd never seen you swim before. I don't think I'd even seen you in the bath, only in the shower when everything was sticky and we were too close, hot, for me to observe you properly.

We don't move together any more, there are no glances dancing between us. I sat heavy on the cool floor, shadows lengthening over me, the surrounding chatter soothing, music lifting over the glossy heads. It buoyed me up on its ebbs and flows and allowed me to eventually move through the room unnoticed.

I clutched my freshly poured drink, trying not to look like I was looking for anyone. The heat slid down my throat. A heady, sweet taste of rot followed, not unpleasant. I was filling up as I glided through the hours, a warm face and cold hands. Corners cradled me as my impatience prevailed. I waited it out.

If I paid attention I could feel the rhythm of the evening, subtly shifting as the sky darkened. Still content, guests continued talking, but with their bodies visibly aware of the rising music. There wasn't any water. I don't think anyone could be bothered to walk to the sink out the back. Leaving the sweet sweat of the room would break the moment, guests trying to sustain the the feeling, voices raising, keener and keener to entertain.

People were unravelling. Shoes strewn across the floor for no reason other than the length of the evening. Hair tumbling over eyes and make-up blurring at the edges. More touching. Hands on waists now, mouths closer to ears and eyes moving uncontrollably up and down bodies. Legs and breasts and shoulders.

I made it out and down the stones then into the persistently icy waters. The cut on my arm stung as I waded in.

As the mist of drink lifted from my body I swam calmly towards the east side of town. I had barely made it to the next groyne when I stopped to float until the sky darkened further, rich hues of blue making their way in streaks across the sky, edges tinged with pink. It was like I didn't have any feet. The daytime sun hadn't managed to cut through the chill, and, breeze picking up, I awkwardly made my way back across the stones. I peeled off my green pants, shoving them into my bag, then I pulled my trousers over my bum and zipped them up, hoping the damp patches would dry quickly when I returned.

Laughing, she approached. Head thrown back and hands following, some kind of real laughter I hardly remembered. Her eyes remained sharp, taking in the surroundings and never allowing anyone to outshine her. She had a tightly controlled presence that scared me, but one slip of movement could betray her and I watched for these vigilantly, scanning her eyes for the familiar flash, always convinced it was coming.

To get back inside we'd have to move through the windowless corridor, stand ourselves in that pinky light before emerging into the room again. As we stood, the sea air flew over the exposed coastline and hit our faces. I desperately wanted to be inside, but as soon as I was the walk from fresh to stale air seemed like a waste of movement.

I thought of your limbs, the careful way you carried them, the way this made me feel a mess; I'd sometimes forget myself and throw up my arms in frustration. Or perhaps this was just to disrupt your stillness.

We were both sitting in the tight corridor, backs against the wall and damp with sweat. The fabric at the back of our knees wrinkled and limp, and if we stretched out our feet they would touch the opposite wall. I was closer than I normally dared. Eyes level because we were both seated, me with my chin resting on my knees as I looked at you.

Its funny how people always end up sitting on the floor.

152

As if being closer to the ground were somehow safer. More of your body's surface area next to the cool floor, supportive. Bits of exposed skin – ankles, maybe a calf – chilled by the concrete, unforgiving.

Her hands were on my waist.

She touched the back of my neck, sliding her fingers up into my hairline until I could feel the cold metal of her rings pressing into me. Tight fit. She pulled my hair then slowly removed her fingers, moving them lightly over my shoulder, coming to rest on my arm. Whispering in my ear, making me blush thinking of the pattern those rings had made across my thigh. Purple like heather and surprisingly bright.

Thick hair, freshly cut, with blunt ends ending above her collarbone. I grabbed a chunk at the back of her head and pulled it back, watching as the tendons in her neck became more pronounced. The winter had been long and when I'd last been this close to her skin it was pale, tinged with blue in the cool light of the street lamps, tops hidden by a covering of snow. We'd watched *All About Eve*. Watched Margot undercut by delicious Eve, not seeing ourselves in either of them but wanting to. White shoulders edged with *broderie anglaise*; nestling in the stiff black silk that stood upright, like a collar. Those beautiful round shoulders lost on her.

Gripping my ankle, you dragged me across the floor towards you.

Then I pulled my hand out of her mess of hair and let it linger in the ends, briefly, gently tugging as I let go. Sliding my hand down her back, only just making contact. I remembered what it was like to stroke her face in the dark, feeling the soft skin stretched over her jaw bone. Her flat was close, a ten-minute walk though the edge-of-town streets and lying in her bed had made me feel like I was floating at sea, water filling three quarters of the window frame. Blissful on the occasions where the sun poured through the glass and onto the duvet, a pool of glow to hold me.

Take off all my clothes and push me under the swell.

Finally I slipped away, out the heavy door and into the salt spray carried on the quickening wind. My car waited in the early evening light but I decided to walk the nearly three miles home. Imagining being so close that I could unhook her belt and feel the warmth of the skin underneath, maybe a thin, wrinkled band of sweat left from the brief spurt of dancing she'd let herself take part in. Then I'd rest my head against her, the powdery smell of washing powder mingling with skin.

Lapping over my skin it stings and tightens. Sometimes I can see my hands beneath, the pale circles of my knees bobbing in the current; in winter murky, brownish-grey and heavier. The thick scoops of sky weighing down the air, seemingly compressing the space between the sea surface and the belly of the clouds. Freezing me from the outside in, breathless and tense my brisk movements condense into one. The temperature renders me almost unconscious. I can't remember how I lifted my feet off the ground and allowed myself to temporarily float, ecstatic. The stubborn numbness in my hands and feet the only way I am sure that I dragged off my clothes and sunk into the wet.

If there's a touch of salt in the breeze I can't resist. Stuck in the tightness of my clothes like it's a skin.

Scoliosis
Rica March

TWO SURGERIES AND COUNTLESS EXAMINATIONS MEANT THAT WHEN I WAS DECLARED HEALTHY AT SIXTEEN, I HAD SEPARATED MYSELF COMPLETELY FROM MY OWN BODY.

FOOD WAS JUST FUEL SO IT DIDN'T MATTER WHAT I ATE.

I COULDN'T CONNECT IN PHYSICAL RELATIONSHIPS.

NOT SLEEPING GAVE ME A SENSE OF CONTROL I HADN'T FELT SINCE BEFORE THE DIAGNOSIS.

OF COURSE IT DIDN'T WORK.

IF ANYTHING I TRAPPED MYSELF EVEN FURTHER IN MY OWN BODY.

I JUST DIDN'T KNOW WHAT ELSE TO DO.

I WAS ALONE.

I WAS THE ONLY ONE WHO COULD FIND ME.

A FEW YEARS BACK, I STARTED RECLAIMING MYSELF.

WITH FOOD.

WITH DYE AND HAIR CLIPPERS, INK AND PIERCINGS.

I WAS MARKED FOR LIFE AT THIRTEEN. NOW I'M MAKING MY OWN MARKS.

ONE DAY I'LL OWN MYSELF AGAIN.

157

XIII

心意気

My first tattoo.
"Bravery at heart"
I got it when I was
nineteen, right before
I applied for art school.

A recent addition for
my 33rd birthday on
Friday the 13th.
Both the rooster and
the rowan are magic
symbols in Swedish
folklore.

D.U.C.K.
A tribute to my
favorite cartoonist
DON ROSA
which in turn is a
tribute from him to
CARL BARKS.

Back in 2010,
I spent a month
in Pennsylvania.
I came back with
this tattoo and
a girlfriend.

Cat skull
My cat died last
summer.
One day I'll get
this in her memory

Stockholm in my heart ♥
I've wanted this tattoo for
years, but the timing hasn't
been right.
I love my city.

Rise Up and Shine
Sami Çapulcu

Sleep is in society's spotlight. If you Google the phrase 'are we getting enough', then 'sleep' is probably your top autocomplete. And the world isn't short on advice. There are more TED talks[1] and *New Scientist* articles[2] on 'sleep' than on 'exercise'. Whether it's via the time-honoured tradition of think-pieces, or the new-fangled approach of sleep tracking apps, suggestions for better sleep management are coming from all directions.

In the last few decades, two new trends have taken over the realm of sleep advice: one is around 'national sleep debt', focussing on how our lack of sleep is harming our economy, and the other is 'sleep hygiene', essentially boilerplate advice to improve sleep.

These new terms highlight an ongoing shift in how we think about sleep, which is becoming more and more linked to **productivity** and **profit**, a connection that is having a negative impact on our wellbeing. But to be able to see these links, we need to unpack what we think about when we think about sleep. What society deems 'healthy sleep' isn't simple medical fact, rather our ideas about sleep are a rich tapestry made up of social and historical norms.

Historical justifications for sleep have varied. A way for the gods to contact us. A way for our bodies to heal the day's afflictions. A means to separate ourselves from devils.[3] Sleep can operate as a **symbol**; for example, of intimacy when we negotiate co-sleeping with partners, or of tension if our preferences clash (late vs early, cuddling vs avoiding, wriggling and rolling around vs being a sleep log). Sleep can also operate as a **tool**, whether to socially condition, such as in our attempts to push young children into sleeping in a consolidated

1   423 for sleep vs 338 for exercise.

2   14,400 for sleep vs 8,540 for exercise (cf. 63,500 for cancer, 2,980 for Alzheimer's).

3   Seriously. The Prophet Muhammad (pbuh) said, 'Take a short nap, for Devils do not take naps' [Sahih al-Jamie. al Albani 1647].

chunk, or in sleep deprivation as a method of torture.

So, sleep is multivalent. And we can understand it better by looking at its place in history.

Valorising Wakefulness

Around the 1800s, an idea took off that saw 'excessive sleep... as a mark of slothfulness'. This idea had been growing since the birth of wage labour – time for sleep is taken from time for work. In the words of labour historian Alan Derickson, the push to 'frame the issue as a simple choice between productive work and unproductive rest' was driven by such luminaries as Thomas Edison.

Edison waged a small-scale war against sleep. He said sleep was an 'inefficient and immoral indulgence' and personally aimed to sleep no more than four hours a night. Not only was he content to work himself to the bone, he used his role as the boss of multiple companies to harass staff into following his sleep regime. Edison even went so far as to employ 'watchers' to hunt down napping staff and drag them back onto the shop floor.

Sadly, this valorising of wakefulness didn't die with Edison. History has given us many torch-bearers for the 'sleep is the enemy of work' mantra. Short sleeping is a skill ascribed to geniuses throughout history – Da Vinci, Tesla, Buckminster Fuller, Benjamin Franklin to name a few. A lot of these are just baseless assertions, which just goes to show how barely sleeping is a modern idea of success.

Exhaustion isn't a natural badge of honour. It takes effort to make it laudable for workers to martyr their wellbeing on the altars of capital. Nowadays, masculinity (and its valuing of sacrifice) does a lot of that heavy lifting. This 'manly wakefulness'[4] thrives in the polyphasic sleeping movement. The basic idea is to replace our modern 'monophasic' sleep pattern – i.e. sleeping in one consolidated block – with lots of little short bouts of sleep throughout the day and night. One 'Uberman schedule' involves six naps of no more than thirty

4   Alan Derickson, *Dangerously Sleepy, Overworked Americans and the Cult of Manly Wakefulness,* (University of Pennsylvania, 2013)

minutes each (typically at 2am/pm, 6am/pm, and 10am/pm) –
a bleakly eugenicist title for an anti-laziness programme.

Polyphasic sleep is truly the arena of 'Silicon Valley types
eager to milk as many productive hours from the day as
possible'.[5] Unlike Edison's time, however, we now have a lot
more reliable information about the health impacts of not
sleeping. Attempting polyphasic sleep will lead most people
to sleep deprivation, which has some pretty severe impacts
(see later). The continued existence of this trend shows just
how powerful the obsession with productivity can be.

Alternative Histories

Sleep isn't just a bellwether for our productivity-obsessed
society. Other approaches to sleep have always played out
alongside those pushed by the worse angels of our nature.

An experiment in a sleep lab in Bethesda, Maryland shone
a light on a different framing of sleep in the early 1990s.[6]
Dr Thomas Wehr confined volunteers to a totally dark room
for fourteen hours a day for four weeks. By the end of their
time, participants had slipped into a 'segmented' or 'biphasal'
sleep pattern – sleeping in two chunks, with a one to three
hour break in the middle. People tended to use this break for
'quiet contemplation', as their bodies surged with prolactin, a
hormone linked to calmness.[7] One sleep researcher said that
'people who experienced that "anti-nap" during the night
said that the next day, they experienced true wakefulness for
the first time'.

As people slipped into this pattern so quickly, and found
it so gratifying, it raises the question why this isn't how we
currently sleep. It turns out that our approach of monophasic sleep is pretty unusual within the animal kingdom. Wehr's
theory is that our consolidated sleep has its roots in our 'arti-

5   Jamie Ducharme, 'People are sleeping in 20-minute bursts to
boost productivity. But is it safe?' (*Time*, 2018) <www.time.com/5063665/
what-is-polyphasic-sleep/>

6   Thomas Wehr, 'In short photoperiods, human sleep is biphasic'
(*Journal of Sleep Research*, 1992)

7   And breastfeeding. And sex. It's multi-purpose. Like sleep!

ficial long photoperiod'.[8] In other words, Edison is still managing to affect our sleep from his grave as it's the technology he popularised – electric artificial lighting – that is so strongly influencing our sleep structure now.

This conclusion gels with the investigations of historian Roger Ekirch, who found evidence of 'interrupted sleep' peppered throughout the history of Western civilisation, which abruptly stopped around the time that electric lighting took off.

Wehr called the break period 'non-anxious wakefulness'. In medieval England, it was the watch; in medieval France, *dorveille*. The gap was used to think, to interpret dreams, to write, read, pray. Benjamin Franklin used his wakesleep to 'take cold-air baths', i.e. open his windows naked. But the watch was also used for more social activities like visiting neighbours or having sex (the sixteenth century physician Thomas Cogan even advised that sex was better in the wakesleep, as by then 'the meate is digested').

Is there a Crisis?

The negative effects of sleep deprivation have been known for centuries. In the sixteenth century, Scottish witch hunters would 'wake' suspected women, depriving them of sleep for days until their hallucinatory ramblings pulled them onto the stake. With modern science, we've been able to quantify more than ever before the perils of not getting enough sleep.

Basically, everything in your body can tank if you don't get enough sleep. Sleep deprivation is linked to memory problems, a higher risk of accidents, blunted creativity, reduced alertness, a less effective immune system, and other cognitive and health impairments. Your inflammation response kicks up, your telomeres shorten, your hormones get out of whack, and your risk of multiple conditions (diabetes, various cancers, depression, heart disease etc.) jumps. And the impacts aren't all personal slow-burners: four per cent of adult drivers

8   Thomas Wehr, 'In short photoperiods, human sleep is biphasic' (*Journal of Sleep Research*, 1992)

in the US have fallen asleep while driving in the last month.[9]

Often this is where sleep advice ends: sleep is necessary, so flog yourself until you get enough. But is it even true that we're not getting enough sleep?

In a 2013 sleep survey, psychologist Richard Wiseman found that forty per cent of people are sleep deprived, defined as getting less than seven hours of sleep, or taking less than five minutes to get to sleep, or needing an alarm clock to wake up in the morning. When Wiseman re-ran the study in 2014, the stat had jumped up to over fifty per cent – with an even higher rate of deprivation in young adults.[10]

One of Wiseman's hypotheses for this jump is smartphones – the blue light they emit affects melatonin production in our brain, which in turn impacts our ability to sleep. However, technology panics harking back to a healthier age should always be taken with a pinch of salt. After all, Plato thought that writing would 'create forgetfulness in the learners' souls'. In the late 1800s, George Beard thought that telegraphs, steam engines and the pace of modern life were causing all manner of social problems, and so he created a catch-all condition 'neurasthenia'. However, according to sleep researcher Michael Grandner, we are only sleeping 'in the range of 15 minutes' less than our parents' generation. This therefore implies that sleep deprivation is quite common, even if our phones aren't necessarily throwing us off a sleep precipice.

'No Norm is Normal'

The gist of 'sleep hygiene' is that there is a standard for a 'healthy night's sleep' shared across everyone, and there are universally agreed ways to achieve it. But the reality is not so simple. Even a cursory glance at the concept highlights cracks in the idea of 'normal sleep'. If one in three adults are sleep deprived at any one time, then what is 'normal'?

For instance, it is relatively new for sleep to be a solo ac-

9   Centers for Disease Control and Prevention, 'Drowsy Driving', <www.cdc.gov/features/dsdrowsydriving>

10   Richard Wiseman, *Night School: The Life-Changing Science of Sleep*, (London: Macmillan, 2014)

tivity – communal sleep used to be the norm. Sleeping one to two people to a room used to be a luxury many couldn't afford until the last century – and that group set-up may be a path we are rediscovering ourselves, in the era of smartphones and social media. In Japan, co-sleeping with children is still common, at least until school age. After the 2011 tsunami, many survivors reported that sharing a communal sleeping space in the shelters helped them relax and regain their normal sleep pattern.

Sleep norms don't just vary across time – they still vary across cultures and countries. Napping at work is more acceptable in Japan – sadly not something that's caught on in the UK yet. Variations in light levels in the Antarctic, the land of the midnight sun, can shift a researcher's biological sleep window by four hours. At its most earthly extreme, when we're totally separated from natural light, people's days have been seen to extend to 48 hours! Off-world, the first moonlanders were too excited/uncomfortable to sleep.

Should everyone aim for the same amount of sleep? Not really. For one, sleep varies across age. From the age of twenty or so, people's need for sleep tends to ramp down from around ten hours to more like seven or eight. About two per cent of adults can even thrive on a few hours of sleep a night, due to a gene mutation on DEC2 (to find out if you're one of these people, try camping without electric light for two weeks, and see what your sleep pattern settles down to).

Should everyone aim for the same bedtime? Again, this varies by age. In puberty, sleep time tends to shift later, then back earlier again as we age. Some even think that this age variation is an evolutionary advantage, meaning someone will be awake at any time, dubbed the 'poorly sleeping grandparent' hypothesis. Ideal sleep time also varies by 'chronotype' – around fifteen per cent of people are strongly morning 'larks', and around twenty per cent are strongly evening 'owls', and the rest fall in the middle.[11]

11   Stephanie Vozza, 'How to Figure out Exactly What Time of Day You'll Be Most Productive' <www.fastcompany.com/40527243/how-to-figure-out-exactly-what-time-of-day-youll-be-most-productive>

Almost none of the so-called norms around sleep stand up to much scrutiny.

The Myth of Control

Most sleep advice follows an 'information deficit' model. It assumes that you would get lots of good quality sleep if only you knew *how*: the 'have you considered sleeping more?' approach.

One reaction to that anxiety is to go to extremes to regain control. This manifests in 'clean sleeping', a trend where people prioritise sleep above all else, often sacrificing friendships and relationships in the process. These 'clean sleepers' still value friendship and love – but they are sacrificing them because work takes up such a large portion of their daily lives.

If good sleep is entirely your responsibility, then the market is more than happy to capitalise on that anxiety; the commercial sleep industry has used it to rake in billions. In the words of sleep researcher Dr Neil Stanley, 'essentially, people want to make you anxious to sell products, devices, books. Saying, "A lack of sleep is going to kill you" is a good headline, but there's not a whole lot of evidence for that. We are being sold a dream that we can be in control of our sleep. It's a fairytale.'[12]

Products run the gamut from sleepy teas and scented candles, to fancy mattresses and sleep trackers. You may take heart from the fact that at least an element of good science will come through, with new technology allowing a detailed personal look at our sleep. Sadly though, more data isn't necessarily more helpful.

If you're in a sleep lab, you may get the full polysomnography set-up – devices tracking your brain, eyes, muscles, heart and breathing. But getting strapped into this every night at home is probably a bit much for even the most dedicated quantified-selfer. Instead, home sleep trackers 'only measure movement, which gives no information about what's happen-

12   Nicole Mowbray, '"Any less than 10 hours and I feel grumpy": meet the clean sleepers', (*Guardian*, 2018) <www.theguardian.com/lifeand-style/2018/jan/19/any-less-10-hours-feel-grumpy-meet-clean-sleepers>

ing in the brain – and that's the important place.'[13]

To mask this deficit, home sleep trackers replace the *fidelity* of lab data with a smokescreen of *unreliable accuracy*. Is getting three per cent less deep sleep last night than the night before bad? Do you know how much your movement varies night by night?

This is especially dangerous because if people are told their sleep is bad, they actually sleep less well; this is termed the *nocebo* effect, the evil cousin of the placebo effect. And underneath all that is the problem that keeps cropping up – that even the idea of 'how much sleep is normal' is a difficult one. Neuroscientist Jack Barton summarised:

> *As soon as I tell people that I'm a sleep researcher, I'm usually bombarded with questions like 'How much do we need?' and 'Why do we need to sleep?' – along with an expectation that I can provide a single time and a clear answer. The truth is we are still very much in the dark when it comes to the 'why' and only have a very broad idea for the 'how much'.*[14]

So what can we do?

Our Sleep, Ourselves

As is so often the case, the first step is naming the problem. The effect of individualising sleep difficulties is that we are **alienated** from our sleep. This alienation is so pervasive that just acknowledging it can feel liberating.

Anxiety about not having 'normal sleep' can easily spiral – some anxiety leads to less sleep, which leads to more anxiety, and so on. Taking the idea of 'normal sleep' off a pedestal

13   Nicole Mowbray, '"Any less than 10 hours and I feel grumpy": meet the clean sleepers', (*Guardian*, 2018) <www.theguardian.com/lifeand-style/2018/jan/19/any-less-10-hours-feel-grumpy-meet-clean-sleepers>

14   Jack Barton, 'Why you shouldn't believe everything your sleep tracker tells you', (*Massive Science*, 2017) <www.massivesci.com/articles/sleep-tracker-healthy-bad-sleep/>

can help us resist stigmatising narratives. This approach is starting to affect professional sleep advice. In the words of Russell Foster, a professor of circadian neuroscience at Oxford University: 'Many people wake up at night and panic. I tell them that what they are experiencing is a throwback to the bi-modal [sleeping in two chunks] sleep pattern.'

Furthermore, evidence says that sleep is harder to get if you're a person of colour, if you're working class, if you're a woman, if you don't have the support of a partner and for many other reasons. This is because power structures affect your ability to sleep – via the mechanisms of inconvenient shift work, the stress of precarity, the patriarchal expectation to work a second/third shift, food insecurity, and so on.

An egregious example of this is in northern Canada where indigenous children are forced to start school at the same time as children living in the south, even though in the north they're still in darkness and their bodies are telling them to sleep. When these kids perform less well in school, it's not a lack of innate academic ability. It is a structural sleep imbalance that may have long term harmful effects on their health, what researcher Jessa Gamble calls 'circadian imperialism'.[15]

When people struggle with delayed sleep phase disorder (where sleep doesn't come until 4am or 5am) or 'non-24' (where your circadian day is not twenty-four hours long), it is because they are often disabled by a society that shuts out people with uncommon sleep patterns. But knowing about sleep's diversity 'normalises the experience of those individuals, and sometimes that can be all it takes to get a better night's sleep,' says one sleep resarcher.[16] But also, just because societal power structures are causing the alienation, this doesn't mean that we can't take steps to minimise the harm it causes. Part of the harm of alienation from our bodies, and of the medicalisation of sleep, is that the mechanisms of sleep can all feel like a big mystery. We can reclaim our power around sleep by finding

15   Jessa Gamble, *The Siesta and the Midnight Sun*, (Viking, 2011)

16   Linda Geddes, 'Sleeping less in old age may be adaptation to surviving in the wild', (*New Scientist*: 2017), <www.newscientist.com/article/2140394-sleeping-less-in-old-age-may-be-adaptation-to-survive-in-wild/>

the evidence-based sleep information out there that works for us.

Here are the four most common bits of sleep advice that I share with friends:
• Sleep happens in cycles of around ninety minutes. If you have to sleep less than you'd like, then waking at the end of a cycle can be less jarring than waking mid-cycle – try counting back from when you need to wake up and add a bit to get a good bedtime.
• While alcohol can help you fall asleep, it disrupts your deep and REM sleep – so if you drink at night, try to stop a few hours before you're planning on going to sleep.
• If you are struggling to fall asleep in bed, then just staying in bed trying to force yourself to sleep probably isn't working for you. Some alternatives: stay away from bed until you're feeling really sleepy; try 'paradoxical sleep' i.e. try and lie in bed with your eyes open (blinking is allowed, I'm not a monster); try and distract your brain e.g. count the proverbial sheep, try and think of an animal for every letter of the alphabet, or count back from 100 in threes.
• If you wake up in the night for more than ten to twelve minutes, then instead of staying in bed, get up and do a relaxing thing in low light for around ten minutes (e.g. a jigsaw), then try again. Repeat as necessary.

Science and tips are great, but the core fight isn't with ourselves when we're in bed. The fight needs to start with what we bring from society into the bedroom. You don't owe society your good sleep. Society owes it to you.

We need to reclaim sleep as a tool – away from productivity and profit, and towards a world of wellbeing. And if we truly want to all get a good night's sleep, then the solution doesn't just lie in sleepy tea – it lies in dismantling power structures that impact our sleep, and rebuilding a society that centres our wellbeing over profit and productivity. You can't get a good night's sleep under capitalism.

In Search of Flight
Aki Schilz

I: The Icarus Complex

> *Look how they are reckless in this taming*
> *of gravity*
> *[...]*
> *you who are human*
> *and must falter in the presence*
> *of such beauty, tell me you have dreamed*
>
> *of lifting your left foot closer*
> *to flight*
> from 'In Defence of Dancing' by Ocean Vuong[1]

***

Google reveals countless entries for 'why can't humans fly?'. Forums littered with web-surfing, landlocked humans seeking answers from self-declared experts, all soul-searching and fevered with desire. Articles from more reputable sources (*New Scientist, Aeon, Yale Scientific*) bear titles like 'The Icarus Complex', 'The Art of Flying', 'Flying without Wings', with bewildering details from culture and technology commentators on the thinking and engineering at the forefront of innovation in achieving human flight. In one such article, there is an alarming description of a workable method fusing techniques in modern reconstructive surgery to 'fabricate human wings from human arms'.[2] Mutilating the body – to become more than a body – to become like a bird. As a by-the-bye, the article informs its readers that the results would be strictly cosmetic. The wings would be non-functioning,

1   Ocean Vuong, 'In Defense of Dancing', (Guernica, 2012) <www.guernicamag.com/in-defense-of-dancing/>

2   Samuel O. Poore, 'The Morphological Basis of the Arm-to-Wing Transition', (*The Journal of Hand Surgery*, 2008)

purely serving a deep-seated desire to make the body, if it cannot actually be made to gain flight, appear like it might. Using calculations of weight to strength ratios, another article bluntly declares: 'our species will never be able to take flight unaided'.[3]

And yet, we yearn. We dream.

There are fifty documented instances of attempts at flight before 1800 (Clive Hart, *The Prehistory of Flight*). And even in the centuries before these attempts, depictions of flying creatures, half-human, half-bird, appear in religious art and in myths and legends across cultures, from twelfth-century winged cherubim in Europe to the Kinnara of South East Asia, winged Mesopotamian gods, the bird-like Chinese thunder god Lei Gong and the fearsome Teigu haunting the forests and mountains of Japanese folklore. Some attempts at making flight possible for humans, like Da Vinci's ornithopters, focus on machinery as an aid, but many centre on the body itself: the body as vehicle, catalysed through mechanisms that would click us out of the pull of gravity, or else, when tumbling, prevent us from succumbing to that dark force that claims the lives of falling souls: gravity. We become angels in these dreams, paintings and inventions. We are redeemed. When we fly, we are absolved. We are free. We are free of the earth, and of the body. In dance, this moment happens at the zenith of a leap or a bound. The weightless, shimmering possibility and power of this shutter-click moment:

> *The triumph of recovery from the fall occurs at the moment of suspension when the person asserts his [or her] freedom from the powers of nature.*
> Stanley Cohen

In another article, I find that the first mass producer of BASE suits was a company trading under the name BirdMan International, some eighty years after Franz Reichelt's fatal

3   Payal Marathe, 'Q&A: Why Can't Humans Fly', (*Yale Scientific*, 2013) <http://www.yalescientific.org/2013/03/qa-why-cant-humans-fly/>

attempt to parachute dive from the Eiffel Tower in 1912. What reckless ambition would drive a man to stake his own life on the possibility of flight? We want to be birds. We wonder why we are not birds. We are willing to die in the attempt to be more like birds. In America, it is illegal to BASE jump from many of the prime spots, for instance in national parks, and if you try, you risk having vital and potentially life-saving equipment confiscated, as well as leaving loved ones to cover the cost of recovery in cases where a jump proves fatal. So, furtively, at dawn-break and dusk across the vastness of nature reserves, humans in bird suits spread their arms like saints and fling their bodies off cliffs and into the unknown. At present, the chances of dying in a BASE jump are 1 in 60.

On the current BirdMan website, the landing page features this quotation, not on flight, but on dance:

> *And those who were seen dancing were thought
> to be insane by those who could not hear the
> music.*
> Friedrich Nietzsche

And in a photo of the wing suits in action, the mosaic of human bodies spread like starfish against a filtered sky, I am reminded of a choreographed dance. A dozen hard-edged Loie Fullers, the softness of her colourful wings blown stiff by G-force. Bodies perfectly synched. Suspended. In triumph.

II: Flighting the Body

In 2014, I walked into an Ana Mendieta exhibition and felt myself falling, dizzy with déjà vu, beneath a video artwork of her body covered in feathers, battling waves in the ocean, listless and then with purpose. I understood. I understood this was her body, and with her body she was escaping the body, tracking the waves, the shore, her own limits. The feathers fluttered, stuck to her skin, were bright against the water on the small black and white screen. In another, this time still, image, there was a space where her body had been in the grass of a Mexican plain. In its place, a shallow indent

171

and a crop of white flowers, sparse as breath.

It is thought that humans' ability to use sensory input to form a conscious awareness of a bird's-eye view of our own bodies lies at the origin of our (curiously) collective dream to fly. Of persons interviewed after near-death experiences, all interviewees have reported a sensation of hovering, or flying. I was out-of-body, they say. It was an out-of-body experience and I saw myself, from above. I could see my body and like in a dream, it was at once me, and not me, and I, the hovering, flying me, was me, too, I think. In that moment I was myself, and not myself, Ana, and not Ana. I was out of my body. I was flying.

I remembered, suddenly, a dance I had choreographed during my brief time with a small company in Oxford. At one point the music rises and I climb onto my partner's body, feet planted on his hips, then standing tall on his shoulders, before corkscrewing forwards. When he reached up to hoist me towards the spotlights, I wanted to keep climbing towards them, to reach beyond them. For a moment, on show night, I thought I might be able to. The spotlights were like three bright moons above me. But I folded, and fell.

III: Dance is a Song of the Body

As upright creatures, we are already vertical, poised, ready for the Next Step, having already crawled our way to standing. We feel we have earned this. We use the springboards available to us to push off from the earth, defying God and gravity: in parkour it is the urban landscape that acts as our sprung floor to somersault off, to spin dizzy twists hundreds of feet in the air from mirrored rooftops and half-crumbled terraces. In athletics we award precious medals to those who can jump the highest, or the farthest. *Maintain the illusion of flight for more than we think is humanly possible and I shall grant thee gold.* As children, we held our breath and jumped, in gardens, in parks, on streets, eyes squeezed shut, thinking if we managed to stay afloat for longer than a couple of seconds, we would remain in the air. We sit in large darkened rooms to watch ten-foot high characters cutting through

172

beautifully shot nightscapes of the world's biggest cities, capes trailing behind like comets. We ooh and aah and practise Superman poses in the mirror at home.[4] We are promised by ad companies who have invested millions spying on our dreams and mining our greatest desires that 'Red Bull gives you wings'. Who among us hasn't entertained the mad hope that... it might?

When I was little, I would see *The Nutcracker* every Christmas with my friend Mary-Jane. Afterwards, we would imagine we were ballerinas, jumping, drunk with the glut and glitter of Sugar Plum Fairy-dust, through the bar and the foyer. I wanted to be Clara on her sleigh, flying through the night, pirouetting into a new, magical, beautiful, world. I had started to dance at the age of two, enrolled in a local ballet school. Even then, somehow I knew that this was the closest I would ever come to flying.

Google search: dancers who look like they are flying.
About 4,230,000 results (0.64 seconds)
Click on: Images.

IV: Breaking

> *Look, it shines in the gloom, far ahead, a vision*
> *of wholeness, ripeness, like a giant melon, like*
> *an apple, like a metaphor for breast in a bad sex*
> *novel; it shines like a balloon, like a foggy noon,*
> *a watery moon, shimmering in its egg of light.*
>
> *Catch it, put it in a pumpkin, in a high tower,*
> *in a compound, in a chamber, in a house, in a*
> *room. Quick, stick a leash on it, a lock, a chain,*
> *some pain, settle it down, so it can never get*
> *away from you again.*
> from 'The Female Body' by Margaret Atwood

4   According to a 2016 US survey, flying comes in second on a list of most desired superpowers. A similar poll taken in the UK puts it fourth, after invisibility, healing ability, and time travel.

'Flying body' brings up only one image of an actual body in flight. It is a woman, hair obscuring her face. She is hinged over a cluster of pastel-coloured balloons as if noosed from it, as if resisting the uplift. In the picture, the unyielding physicality of the body is made obvious. I feel uncomfortable looking at it, and pinch the plumpness around my belly, eye the pale wastedness of my thighs, once strong and muscled. Had I ever been a dancer-as-body to begin with? I couldn't claim to have attained the rigidity and self-control ballet demanded of me, and it felt I had failed, and kept on failing with the passing years; the softening and expansion, the stretch marks like pale feathers. And there was another thing, I was realising only now as I looked at this woman with her face obscured, as if not wanting to be seen. It was Martha Graham who called dance 'discovery, discovery, discovery' – and yet discovery, surely, requires a gaze meeting the object; a completion. Stopping – no longer dancing – had made me incomplete and, at the same time, impossible to bring to completion. No longer in service to the spectator, my body, unobserved, had wasted, a half sketch in half light, loosed at the edges. I had forfeited my right to discovery.

Halfway down the page of the same results, a half-sketched bird in charcoal catches my eye. The incompleteness makes it seem, somehow, more alive to me, more... in flight. A young Singaporean photographer's Surreal-ity series shows her running along a beach, slowly lifting away. Yet it is the photographs of dancers I am drawn back to again and again. And some I assume to be dancers, but are not. I spot famous faces in one particular series. It is a wonderful discovery. Philippe Halsman's *Jump* series catches famous people jumping. Among the jumpers are Audrey Hepburn, Grace Kelly, Ava Gardner, Dean Martin, Eartha Kitt and Maurice Chevalier... Philippe explains his 'jumpology' theory, and something in my own body buzzes in recognition:

> *In a jump, the subject, in a sudden burst of energy, overcomes gravity. He cannot simultaneously control his expressions, his facial and his limb*

muscles. The mask falls. The real self becomes
visible. One has only to snap it with the camera.

Jump, hop, leap, bound, sissonne...

In the film *Dancers* there is a scene where Mikhail Baryshnikov simply practices jumping. He uses the sprung floor
almost as a trampoline, gaining traction, jumping higher and
higher. I have watched the scene many times and felt the same
giddy something I felt when I visited the Ana Mendieta exhibition, and the same feeling again when I saw Carlos Acosta
on stage for the first time. He was hardly human when he
jumped, when he leapt, with the energy of a stag. I return to
the YouTube clip of Baryshnikov. In the comments section,
someone has written: 'Proof that Baryshnikov could indeed
fly!' I am in a fever dream. My body remembers practising
just this. For years. Ballet, contemporary, performance art in
flamboyant costumes in which I flung my body across rooms,
art galleries, stages, fields. The earth as a platform, the body
as a platform, a hand, a leg, a sprung floor, a tensed forearm.
Pushing the body outside of itself, if even for a brief, joyous,
delirious moment. Practising trying to fly.

And to disrupt. To disrupt the triumvirate of geometry,
extension, and measured harmony. To disrupt the gaze of the
viewer. To disrupt the historic containment of the female body
(Chastity with a sieve held on her lap, holding but not releas-
ing water), the regulation of the body, the body in the mirror.
Ripping the self from the mirror and shouting into the stars
we swing ourselves towards, ready to fly or fall. Ready, if we
fall, to recover.

> *Falling away from and returning to a state of*
> *equilibrium constitutes the continuous flux in*
> *the human body: giving in to and rebound from*
> *gravity.*
> Doris Humphrey

V: Unbreaking

Google searches for 'Dance and flying' bring up surprisingly little. But below the search engine optimised results come the 'searches related to dance and flying', which begin with these top three searches:

Modern dance **jumps and leaps**
Contemporary dance **jumps** names
Impressive dance **jumps**

A joyous monochrome still catches Rita Hayworth leaping over Fred Astaire towards the camera, on set of the film *You Were Never Lovelier*. But it's clear that she's jumping to land. In most of the other photographs that come up – the photos of dancers – the images have been shot in such a way as to suggest suspended motion, anti-gravity; flight. The idea is that these bodies have lifted away from the ground and away from the pull of gravity. They've become unstuck. They are free.

> *the study of dance [...] is, after all, a kind of*
> *living laboratory of the study of the body – its*
> *training, its stories, its ways of being and being*
> *seen in the world.*[5]

At night, I dream of them, photograph after photograph of bodies in jumps, twists, splits. A gentle rain of glossy squares, all effortless – far more so than I was ever able to achieve over twenty-two years of training, of muscles hardening and softening and my body shifting shape many times. In my dreams, I am not the girl who could not execute a triple pirouette. I glide, swing, twirl. I am not the girl who, after leaping and landing hard, heard a senior soloist snipe, if you were a little less heavy, you'd have landed that. If I'd dared more, believed in my body, I'd have flown up over her head, shining like a balloon, giant as a melon. I am not the girl who, having put too much or too little resin onto the ends of her pointes, was

5   Ann Daly, 'Unlimited Partnership: Dance and Feminist Analysis', (*Dance Research Journal*, 1991) Vol 23, Issue 1.

over-ambitious with her arabesque one show night and stumbled into the wings, muddling the velvet curtains and landing in the arms of Don Quixote.

In my dreams I am powerful, elegant. I am Carlos Acosta as a stag re-embodied as a doe, drinking from her own reflection and smashing the water to silver. I am Baryshnikov nesting in the wings of Loie Fuller, dazzled with colourful light, I am Jiří Kylián startling Louise Lecavalier mid barrel jump in the sunlit insides of a violin. I am Yves Klein leaping into the void, tumbling through the bodies of Isadora Duncan, Nadezhda Pavlova, Moira Shearer, Pina Bausch, the whole of DV8 Physical Theatre limb by limb, to reclaim the greatest leaps and bounds and tricks. I am breaking the world open, and myself.

Glissade to prepare, *pas de chat*, and break. Break. Break. Fly.

The flying body has broken something, but by doing so, is unbroken. Is unbreakable.

I am practicing being unbreakable. I am practising trying to fly.

Does a Silhouette have a Shadow?
Michael Amherst

*A silhouette is a dark outline against a light background.
It is a body seen in profile as the light fails, indiscernible as
anything other than a phantom of the original. It is a form
visible as a dark shape against a canvas or screen. It is a dark
shadow, but it is not a shadow itself. A shadow is a dark pro-
jection caused by a body coming between rays of light and a
surface, such as the ground.*

Illness reshapes our world. It affects our faculties and our
perception. I recognise this in manic, elated days for which
I do not know the source. Is it the drugs? The gabapentin?
The steroids? Is it simply the sun? I question reality and my
own sincerity. Is this me or is this given me by something
else? All I know is that I overflow like a vase left under a tap,
slowly emptying and emptying at the same time as filling up
and up. Why does literature pay illness so little attention, asks
Virginia Woolf[1], when it remakes our world in much the same
way as love?

I have three chronic health conditions: psoriasis, psoriatic
arthritis and EBV viraemia. People often mishear EBV as HIV.
Epstein-Barr virus is part of the herpes family, and is best
known for causing glandular fever. The symptoms manifest
themselves so like HIV that every time I am admitted to hospital it is the first thing they test for.
'Is there any chance you could have HIV?', they ask.
I have now been told I would be better off if I had HIV.
This previously felt unsayable. 'If you had HIV we'd know
what it was,' my doctor said. 'And we could treat it.'
As it is, we do not know that EBV viraemia even is my condition. It may only be a consequence – what the medics call
'a bystander' – of something else. But this is also misleading,
because the EBV does not simply look on. It grows and repli-

1   'On Being Ill', Virginia Woolf, *Selected Essays* (Oxford: Oxford
University Press, 2009).

179

cates in my blood until it is so systemic that my body does not have the capacity to fight any other infection. Lymph nodes swell around my neck and in my groin, ulcerations flower across my throat so that it is painful to swallow. I develop a moderate fever and night sweats.

'Is there any chance you could have HIV?', the doctors ask.

Maurice Merleau-Ponty[2] said that our bodies are the prism through which the world is experienced. My body is the capacity of my existence. It is what makes me relative to the world, locating me in time and space. We are incapable of detachment, or objectivity, for our embodiment is our only means of experience. It, 'is the "flaw" in this "great diamond", the world; because perception is the capacity whereby there is a world it cannot be just another fact within the world'. My embodied perception cannot be thought around. It cannot be willed away or willed different, for it is the very foundation of my will. To presume otherwise is to presume the position of God. It is the shaky ground upon which I stand.

A silhouette and shadow are identical twins. Both require a body. A silhouette is a body cloaked in the darkness of a fading light, while a shadow is cast by a body bathed in light as it obscures its relationship with a surface. An evening makes a silhouette of the skyline, while the sun behind a building casts a long shadow across the ground. But as the sun sets and the light dims the silhouette grows darker and heavier, its shadow consumed by the growing night. In this sense, a silhouette has a shadow.

Nothing so vividly reminds us of the fact of our body as its failure. Sufferers of chronic illness cannot forget we have a body: it reminds us in every act of defiance, every instance of pain, every refusal to our will. If our bodies are the prism, then our health plays a part in the refraction. Woolf is right –

2   Maurice Merleau-Ponty, *The World of Perception* (London: Routledge Classics, 2004).

illness draws our attention to the relativity of our experience of the world.

When I am well, I forget how my pain feels. In the absence of arthritis, I remember only vague swellings, an ache. It is a side street in my neighbourhood, rather than my world. But when it returns it alters all. Chronic illness remakes the quotidian. It gives birth to hundreds of new experiences and makes many others unbearable. It forces me to pay attention to acts of which I am usually unconscious, to somatic knowledge that I ignore. It demonstrates how slight my understanding of the world truly is – that, as Merleau-Ponty observed, it is only known through my body.

My body altered remakes the world in its image. My appreciation of touch – my ability to welcome, desire, reject or even resent contact with another – is shown to be relative. A sudden movement, a change of direction to avoid someone in the street, a brush of coats, a bag hitting me – all feel like an assault. And, in a sense, they are. It is about effort: an effort to withstand, an effort to be, an effort to forebear even the normal things. Yet, when I am well, these things cease to be. Then they are imperceptible: no longer an effort, nor a chore. Only then are they the stuff of everyday life.

We live under a misapprehension – that knowledge is cognitive and to be shaped and assessed by our reasoning faculty. Yet, there is a knowledge that is physical – somatic – one accessible by our body but not our mind. The obvious example is a woman in early pregnancy. Her body knows she is pregnant and nourishes and develops the foetus, well before she 'knows'. My illness has made me aware of my body and its sensations. I've learnt to hear its cries: the bruise that only fades to dark pigmentation, the damp on my pillow as I wake with sweat on my brow, the insomnia that hits when I'm most fatigued – each and all of these are expressions of the virus manifest in my blood. To acknowledge this is to accept alternative means of understanding, a recognition that knowledge does not always need to be known but can be felt. Our reason, and the language which it constructs, may be inadequate to the knowledge that our bodies feel and contain.

Brian Blanchfield[3] draws upon the work of psychoanalyst D. W. Winnicott on feelings and containment when he asks, 'Where is fear, or desire, or grief, if not inside? I know it is within, because I contain it.' Here the body acts as both the repository and medium for feeling, while actively containing – holding in place – feelings as a form of personal, subjective knowledge.

To know does not always mean to understand what it is we know; our bodies can respond and feel without our minds having shaped those feelings into knowledge. What if the body is in possession of knowledge too complex and varied for the limited demands of our mind and its language? What if our reason is the mind's construction in its overmastering need to maintain an illusion of primacy over the body and its secrets?

I can see the cast of my shadow on a sunny day, but I can never see myself in silhouette. Nor can I see my silhouette in reflection, for the light will be too brilliant on the reflected surface. I can see my shadow but not as you see it, just as the way I see and know my embodied self is only ever partial or through an imperfect lens.

The body is the locale of feelings and knowledge. Our understanding of the world is, in that sense, empirical, but it is not the limited kind of empiricism practised by a material science. It is not quantifiable and replicable. It is an empiricism founded in phenomenology, or as Marilynne Robinson observes, 'We know things in the ways we encounter them.'[4]

In some sense, how we encounter things is also how we

3   Brian Blanchfield, *Proxies: A Memoir in Twenty-four Attempts* (London: Picador, 2017).

4   Marilynne Robinson, *The Givenness of Things* (London: Virago, 2015).

encounter ourselves. Increasing numbers of scientific studies demonstrate the effect of upbringing on how we respond to the world and, in turn, how this impacts on our physical health.

For example, inflammatory response is both a key component of the immune system as well as a response to stress. Sue Gerhardt describes the correlation between those whose emotional needs are not met in infancy and the body's inability to regulate inflammation, resulting in increased instances of autoimmune conditions. The failure to process or express emotion becomes a chronic problem, liable to cause a constant exaggerated inflammatory response.

> When anger or distress are not expressed or dealt with in some constructive way, **stress may become chronic** and stress hormone cortisol may remain in the system…This can end up in cortisol levels 'down-regulating'. The resulting 'hypoactive' or sluggish stress response can't then do its normal job of turning off the body's inflammatory response.[5] (My bold)

When I started senior school at thirteen, I ended each school day with my mother, walking our three dogs along the bridle path out of the village. The evenings were beginning to draw in and we would watch the sun set over the escarpment, before cutting through trees and out into fields.

And I'd say: 'I just need quiet. It's so noisy there. There are too many people. I just want to be quiet. Like this.'

And after three days, I stopped going.

A silhouette can appear on a canvas. I enter a room, the moon at my back, and am illuminated in the doorway. The room is split by a screen, a sheet of calico. When a silhouette is cast upon a screen then the light source is divided from its canvas by the body it illuminates. In this way, the silhouette is

5   Sue Gerhardt, *Why Love Matters: How Affection Shapes a Baby's Brain* (London: Routledge, 2015).

also a shadow. A shadow with a shadow. You are on the other
side of the screen. My body casts a shadow at my feet, but this
is not visible to you, on the other side of the screen, observing
my silhouette. I can see the canvas, can discern the differing
qualities of light passing through, but I do not see my image
there. I cannot see my silhouette but I can see my shadow.
You cannot see my shadow, but can see my silhouette.

Stress and depression are both known to trigger the production and release of cytokines into the body. Cytokines are inflammatory proteins produced as part of our immune response. Their release drives inflammation further. At the same time, the cytokine TNF-alpha, the one thought to be responsible for psoriasis and inflammatory arthritis among other conditions, has been found to impede the production of serotonin in the brain. Those suffering from depression and anxiety are thought to have lower serotonin levels than normal.[6] Several studies have described the cyclical relationship between depression in the brain and inflammatory disease – particularly psoriasis and psoriatic arthritis.

The backdrop to this was the nervous breakdown of my favourite junior school teacher. Having previously been one of his 'favourites', he denounced me in lessons to the watching class. Sometimes he'd move onto my parents – describing my father as a drunk and my mother a lunatic.

Later, after he'd been dismissed for writing love letters to another boy, I learnt what being one of his 'favourites' could have meant. Previously he had compared the sexual attractiveness of me and my best friend and found me wanting – something which at age twelve I was all too aware of, I'd just yet to give it a name. I never told this to anyone – for he had voiced aloud what I most feared. So I only told adults about the many ways he assured me I'd be beaten up at secondary school, not his assurance that no girl would ever

6   Melissa Leavitt, 'The link between psoriatic disease and mental illness' (National Psoriasis Foundation, 2015) <www.psoriasis.org/advance/link-between-psoriatic-disease-and-mental-illness>

find me attractive.

Three months later I moved to senior school and after three days stopped going altogether. I was diagnosed with glandular fever. It does not strike me as odd that my body should have fallen into illness. Maybe even welcomed it. However, I know this was not conscious or willed, so much as my mind and body embraced in a shadowy dance.

To both of us – to you and to me – these split shadows are representations. They allude to the (corpo)real. They coexist but their appearances wax and wane with the strength of the light. When the sun is strong, then my shadow is dark and heavy, yet the light too bright for my form to ghost to a silhouette; when the light fades then my body disappears into a partial representation of itself and its shadow bleeds into all the other, lengthened shadows that fall into the dark across the ground.

There is a myth, a fiction, we need to tell ourselves: that our bodies are our own. So strong is my need for a clear, defined agency that I would rather maintain a pretence that renders me culpable than accept a relationship between mind and body so far and mysteriously beyond my control. I cannot stand the idea that I am an organism made up of many shadowy systems.

The physical cannot be argued with. The arid desertification of the psoriasis across my face, the locking of joints that need to be manually turned like a latch – we regard these things as real. Yet, for the mind to have a role in physical illness is suggestive of invention, of the unreal. The erroneous conflation of psychosomatic ailments with hypochondria is indicative of our need for certainty over mystery, mastery over impotence. The paradox is that our bodies are our own, yet strange to us at the same time.

Winnicott wrote, 'A word like "self" naturally knows more than we do; it uses us and can command us.' Here, again, we

185

know more than we know; our language both fails to keep up while alluding to a knowledge out of reach. Adam Phillips believes Winnicott was, 'asserting the presence of something essential about a person that was bound up with bodily aliveness, yet remained inarticulate and ultimately unknowable: perhaps like an embodied soul.'[7]

Shadow and silhouette are both images cast by a single, embodied subject. The totality of these images is less than the subject but the subject can never be seen all at once, in all its forms. Our sight of it, our knowledge of it, is always partial.

What if my illness is a cave, one in which I crawl and hide? If the physical is a manifestation of mental anguish, I fear it may be no more than a convenient excuse. An inconvenient excuse. A respite from the living. But who would invent this? Or rather, how bad must what I'm fleeing be to go to such lengths?

A child can only be ill so long. Gradually the voices turned and stopped being sympathetic. I remember being dragged downstairs and pushed into the back of the car. Someone sat and restrained me, to ensure I didn't jump out while the car was moving. Before I was ill, our family friend, the builder, would always come and hold out his great, dusty hands for me to give him a high-five. I remember the taste of his extra-strong mints, the sound the silver paper made as he peeled it away in one piece, like a bartender with orange twist. He stopped talking to me except to demand why I wasn't at school. I remember the shame of being in the secretary's office, my uniform in a shopping bag and me in just pyjamas as teachers and pupils walked by wondering what it was I was doing. Or rather, not doing. My parents were variously advised to give me a clip round the ear, beat me, let me jump out of the moving car. My cousin said I'd go back when I was ready.

[7] Adam Phillips, *Winnicott* (London: Penguin Books, 2007).

A lack of agency is not something we can bear. The idea that past trauma can dictate future sickness makes medical science feel akin to Calvinism. It is hard to hear about the role my psyche can play in my health without also hearing that I am responsible for it. At the same time, if I have had some unintentional role in my plight then I can feel impelled to try and combat it, or 'fix it' through some alternate force of will.

Following a stay in hospital, I presume my anxiety, my low mood is real. I search for a reason, a problem, something to amend. I am guilty of presupposing that my mood is an entirely mental process. But this mood is physical. This piss that is a deep, spring-dark green is my kidneys flushing out inflammatory markers from my bloods: the toxins, the infection, the waste products from my body healing. I am fatigued by the energy required in recovery. I know from previous episodes of illness that when my body is recovering, my mood dips. In this sense, this is not 'me'. At least, this is not the cognitive 'me', one in charge or one that can find a solution.

My authoritarian impulse to root out and act on a cause is a hindrance, not a help. My mood is a balloon over which I have no control, save that my desire to master it, to keep it in check is what tethers it to the ground. Only when I step back and accept that a fortnight after a hospital admission it is reasonable for me to feel exhausted, rundown and depressed, do I release my grip on the pretence that this is something over which I have control. And, like a balloon, my mood slowly lifts.

Neither a shadow nor a silhouette exist without the other. For even when the other is hidden or obscured, it must be there – if only because each/both are given form by a body and the light that animates it. No night is ever completely dark.

It took an analyst to observe that rather than listening to my body I was driving it to destruction. Enamoured with a story of control, I contrived an agency for myself that was delusional. Any period of remission I believed to be the result of lifestyle change, the outcome of my conscious will in over-mastering my body. I viewed myself with a degree of detachment, an object, one over which I ruled sovereign. Detachment distanced me from feeling, distanced me from pain. Yet a denial of feeling is to deny the body, denial of embodiment a refusal to feel.

My body is not a choice. It is not open to challenge. In an age of self-improvement my body is a reminder of the brute fact of my existence. Anthony Giddens describes the modern obsession to sculpt, hone, craft our bodies as a reflection of our desire for agency.

What might appear as a wholesale movement towards the narcissistic cultivation of bodily appearance is in fact an expression of a concern lying much deeper actively to 'construct' and control the body.[8]

Meanwhile, billion-pound industries tell us all we need do is 'think positive'. All promise that I can be the agent of change. But this willed direction is a myth. Sometimes it is what holds us back. Psychoanalysis teaches us that change can only occur when we give up on change, that the first thing to accept is the fact of ourselves as we are.

I have a vague sense that my body is my greater truth teller. The willed direction of my mind, the voice that chatters on inside my head – narratives, anxieties, a constant locution of forward movement, direction and agency – that is the thing that is false. It is the pain and exhaustion I feel in my limbs and joints that accurately express the fatigue my body feels in the face of a will that oppresses while never meaningfully ruling it.

My body is what makes me relative to the world – it gives me form and locates me in space and time. Those experiment-

8   Anthony Giddens, *Modernity and Self-Identity: Self and Society in the Late Modern Age* (Cambridge: Polity Press, 1991).

ing with cyronics, or body preservation through freezing, are at the forefront of the Cartesian fallacy. The fact of being embodied – in a form that ages, grows weary and dies – is not a flaw. It is how we exist, how we perceive, how we feel. It is both how we relate to the world around us and are in the world around us. At the same time, how and what we feel and perceive is a story written in inflammatory markers, cancers, cytokines and hormones. Our bodies are as revealing as any autobiography.

The body is real, shadow and silhouette its limited image. They are images given form by a body obscuring a light. The body is the subject. The subject is only seen because of the presence of light. And it is through seeing that something can become known. In this way we know the body. We know the body for the light animates it, just as the soul animates the self.

Hiding Places
Umairah Malik

I'm not sure why I kept going there. Old habits die hard. It was never even about the lipstick.

The building had always been a commercial property, restaurants and bars would come and go, set up shop, all with more passion than the last, and yet over the years none of them have succeeded. A lonely corner shop repeatedly inhabited by distinct lonely people, each looking at the next with pity, whispering that it will not be fruitful regardless of the effort put in.

And yet they continued to come.

I found a magazine there beneath a pile of menus whilst waiting to be served. There was an article in it about the importance of loving your body and in the same spread it told me that this red lipstick *this very lipstick* will make me beautiful.

(There are three tubes of that lipstick in the bathroom cupboard at home, a pink, a purple and a nude. The deep purple is the one I use when I cannot hide how I unequivocally feel under this carapace of confidence.)

The owner of the first restaurant had wrinkles around his eyes, greying hair and a hacking cough that would have woken the dead. He'd sit on the doorstep, cigarette between his fingers, taking long, deep breaths, calling out to the neighbours.

His wife wore scarlet on her mouth, a shade I was always too afraid to wear. She laughed and smiled with that rich red colour on her lips, handing out coffee like it was candy on Halloween whilst her hands shook.

The place sailed through the honeymoon phase but people began to prefer going further out into the mainland for their meals, drawn to the vast shopping malls, and he stayed sat on the doorstep, somewhere along the way the cigarette changing into a glass of wine, the glass of wine turning into a bottle.

The lines on his forehead became deeper and deeper, his
191

walk wearier, wife no longer as physically present as she used to be. The neighbours returned from their trips long after closing time, sunset on their cheeks, and laughter in their eyes.

It wasn't long till the windows were boarded up, the for sale sign plugged into the ground, owners long gone to wherever old people go when the world gives up on them.

The next one came along a while later, fresh faced, no wrinkles around the eyes, diploma folded neatly in her pocket, too many big ideas for such a small building in a small town in a small world.

She sat behind the till, laughed with people escaping their mundane lives on Friday nights.

The leaflets she had created dropped through the letterbox, barely having a chance to acquaint with the ground before they landed above used tea bags and yesterday's leftovers.

She wore a dark blue colour on her lips; I heard someone say she looked 'bloody awful' without it. She offered to lend me some, 'all the celebrities are wearing it', and handed me the tube at five past midnight. Apparently it'd match my eyes, because I needed some colour.

So I did. And later on, I stood in my bathroom with only the light from the street lamps outside, staring at the reflection opposite me, wondering who this girl was.

It wasn't long till she too decided to move on, to a bigger building in a bigger town in the same small world.

Before leaving, she pulled me aside, said I could be beautiful if I tried, that 'friends tell each other this kind of thing'.

A local politician comes to the next opening, complete with the local paper, cuts the ceremonial ribbon, and fulfils the obligatory hand-shaking acts. She tells a story of reaching high, the need for working-class people like us to break the good old glass ceiling, her speech complete with wild gestures and dramatic pauses.

She takes a picture with some of us, the ones in headscarves, dark faces, with the young 'uns. I swear I almost hear her whisper it'll do wonders for her publicity, her ratings will
192

soar way higher than she thinks any of us will be going.

The meals that day are on the house, excitement runs through the Muslim owner, the enthusiasm streaming off of him.

I don't remember her name now, the politician, but she sat with us, picking at her food, smiling through the red lipstick that was in the magazine advertisement, laughing louder than necessary, eyes wavering. I read something that night about the visit being about ticking the diversity box.

A few months later she was back in the nationwide papers, arguing for immigration control or something of the sort, wearing the same shade of lip colour she wore when visiting this desolate town. It's similar to one I own, so I put it on, wondering if I could be that self-assured; if I could leave the house without that gnawing feeling still at the forefront.

That night, the Muslim man sat on the doorstep where the first owner used to sit and holds his head in his hands, the shop behind him empty, and the sound of music fooling nobody. What do you do when the world moves on, when time continues and you stay stuck? Are we all pawns in a game we never knew we were playing?

So much time spent being told who we are and who we shall be, the ultimate paradox being the more we try to find control the more we lose it.

That building is a microcosm of this small world, a never-ending cycle that has to be broken by *all of us*.

Yesterday, I walked past the shop, windows boarded up again, for sale sign not in the ground but scrawled on a piece of paper stuck on the door, fighting the force of the wind.

Today, I threw out all my lipstick.

Too Much and Not Enough — An Abridged History of My Breasts

Christina McDermott

[Content note: fatphobia]

Like a lot of people of my generation, I'm an avid podcast listener. Mostly true crime stuff but pretty much any genre interests me if the presenters are engaging enough. My favourite ones tend to be presented by perky American women who speak to you like they're in your living room, splitting a bottle of cheap red wine with you while gossiping about make-up and serial killers.

Recently, many of my regular listens have started advertising bras. Perfect, comfy bras that fit every woman – every back, every tit. 'You'll never wear a better fitting bra!' they reassure me and, for a moment, I believe them. I am thirty-five years old and typically wear a 40GG, although that constantly changes depending on the day of the week, the time of the month and the state of the weather. I listen to these ads, read out by these women who sound so trustworthy, so true, and then use my phone to Google the brand. Turns out the 'perfect bra' is only perfect if you're a size 38F or below. I chuckle grimly to myself and mentally compose a snarky tweet about it, which I'll never send because what would be the point? In the ten years I've been on Twitter, I've lost count of the annoyed tweets I've sent to fashion brands concerning their refusal to accept that bodies don't all come as perfectly calibrated models. And yet I can count on one hand the changes they've made as a result of my anger and the anger of people like me. It's infuriating to constantly repeat yourself to no avail, an experience akin to shouting into a black hole. But most of all, it's incredibly fucking depressing.

And never more so than when it comes to bras. I have always seen the act of wearing one to be a necessary evil, with added emphasis on the evil. I regularly spend upwards of £30 to be prodded and poked by well-meaning bra fitters, only to encounter straps that fall down or twist like sticks of liquorice or bras that dig or poke or leave angry red marks that take hours to fade. The best part of my day is always taking my bra off. There's an incredible sense of release when I ping that strap at my back and unleash my breasts, letting them flop around in all their pale, oversized glory.

For me – and many others like me – finding a comfortable, affordable everyday bra is like (finally) getting around to writing a book, or mastering making doughnuts. It's a great idea in concept but putting in the work to actually achieve it just leaves you feeling exhausted, messy and sore.

I think of all the pieces I've read in women's media raving about 'inclusive' lingerie brands that don't include anyone with breasts that don't meet some kind of prescribed norm, whether too small or too large, chests belonging to people recovering from mastectomies or people who don't fall into a defined gender binary. I think of my own chequered history of bra wearing and how – all too often – I've found myself crying in changing rooms, wishing I could somehow make myself smaller and more feminine. That feeling of being trapped inside a body that is too much yet never enough.

***

1995. I am twelve years old, and my mother has taken me to Debenhams to purchase my first bra. It is a rite of passage informed by various different things. My ballet teacher recently saw me (literally) bouncing around doing my *pliés* and *entrechats* and had a gentle word in my mother's ear – maybe it's time for you to do something about this. Mum works at Debenhams, knows the bra fitter there and entrusts her to do the right thing or, at the very least, have the decency to warm up her hands before assessing the measure of my nascent breasts (I am an avid reader of *Just Seventeen* and have already encountered numerous horror stories of budding boobs being chilled to the core by icy palms and frigid tape measures.)

I stand in the changing room while a kindly woman takes the measure of me, my pale adolescent body aglow under the fluorescent lights that seemed cruelly designed to highlight
196

all your flaws. The positioning of the mirrors in the cubicles means that I can see my evolving form reflected back at me thousands of times, providing multiple views of thousands of different tiny elements of my body to develop complexes about. It is the first time I become aware of this, but it will not be the last. In my thirties, I will try and figure out how many hours of my life I've spent in changing rooms, wriggling in and out of clothing that is too tight, or gapes in the wrong places, or which fastens in a vice-like grip around my chest like a finger trap[1] and then give up because it's just too depressing.

Finally, the fitter (whose hands, thankfully, aren't nearly as chilly as expected) stands back and pronounces to my Mum that I am 'definitely a small B' and trots off to find suitable bras for me to try on while I reel in horror. B? How can I be a B? It is too big and round a letter, too wrong a size. When she returns, the whole affair suddenly feels even worse. What she is dangling in her hands look gigantic – great frothy, lacy white things; a million miles away from the miniscule 'bras' I've seen my peers all wear while they giggle about how grown up they feel wearing them.

My icons right now are Kate Moss, Christina Ricci and Winona Ryder, all beautiful, sylphlike women with tiny waists and breasts like bee stings. It suddenly dawns on me that no matter how much I try to bend it to my will, my body will never be like theirs. Puberty has caused it to evolve into something that I will wrestle with for the rest of my life.

For the first time – but definitely not the last – I look at myself in the mirror and burst into tears.

***

1   Many years later, I will try on a dress for my grandfather's funeral which will refuse to budge over my breasts after I've tried it on. I end up running around in a blind panic, like a cat that's accidentally got a paper bag lodged over its head, frantically live tweeting the experience until a stitch pops and I manage to wriggle myself free. I'd say that I felt like Houdini, but I'm pretty much positive that the master escapologist's act never stretched to getting himself stuck inside a £34.99 ASOS frock.

I have always had large breasts and I have always felt a strange sense of shame about them. And when I say 'large', I do not mean 'a generous handful'. These cups continually runneth over. From an early age, I have viewed them as being 10 per cent blessing and 90 per cent curse. They destroy underwires (I've lost count of the times I've had to throw away bras because a vital piece of their engineering has come loose and is attempting to skewer me like a delicious tit kebab). They make it impossible to buy shirts which don't gape in inconvenient places, mock Marks & Spencers's patented 'no peep' concealed button clothing technology and require me to carry an emergency safety pin in my purse at all times. A few years ago, I ran a half marathon. When I saw the official race day photo of me crossing the finish line, my breasts swung mightily to the left while the rest of my body veered to the right, making it look as though I was being torn apart in a grisly, invisible tug-of-war. I did not purchase the photo.

Their size has defined me for so much of my life, I often wonder what it would be like to wake up and suddenly find that they had shrunk, or that I had finally managed to discover a way to give away parts of them in a timeshare like I'd jokingly discussed with friends. I dream of it longingly – a life of finally being able to wear delicate, silky scraps of lingerie, which would flutter through my fingers before moulding themselves perfectly to my body. Of being able to run without feeling that cramping pain in my lower back. Of men meeting my eyes when they're introduced to me, instead of their glance continually creeping down towards my chest.

I want to say that I hate my breasts, but that would be too simplistic. It would also be wrong. My breasts are part of me and I'm great, ergo they must be great. Right?

But of course, it's never that easy.

***

1996. I am thirteen and watching television with my family. There's a terrible stand-up comedian doing a routine that centres around hastily animated Mattel toy cash-in She-Ra and the fact that she has a tiny waist and huge tits. He goes on repeatedly about how unrealistic it is. How a warrior princess like her couldn't have a figure like that unless she had a really good plastic surgeon because the only women he'd ever seen with tits that large had huge bellies and thunder thighs. The audience laughs riotously while I sit there, folding my arms over my chest as though by doing so, I can shrink myself. It's not that I'm not aware of the fact I have larger breasts than most of my classmates – the boys who sit behind me in music who love to constantly flick my bra straps through my shirt whenever I dare to take off my school jumper off have made me acutely aware of that. I had just never realised before that the situation I'd found myself in was all my fault. My body throbs with adolescent shame. I make a mental note to start cutting out fizzy drinks and stop eating lunch.

1997. I am fourteen. It is Christmas Day and my parents have friends over for post-dinner drinks. Everyone is tipsy and gregarious, and I feel awkward in that way that teenagers always do in the presence of drunken adults. My uncle has brought over someone that he works with who cannot stop staring at me with a look in his eyes that I know, instinctively, to be dangerous. I feel – as I will do many times over the years – panicked and powerless, stuck in a situation I feel utterly out of my control. Everyone is dancing to terrible Christmas music in the living room and he moves towards me and, invites me to dance. As he tries to pull me towards him, he gropes my right breast. It is quick, out of sight and for a moment I wonder if I've imagined it. But then I see the leer in his eyes and it feels like poison is blossoming in my stomach. I want to scream, kick him in the bollocks, call him a pervert, make the mother of all scenes. But who would believe me? After all, his wife is here. He's just had a bit to drink. He's just being a bit friendly. I go up to my room, crawl into bed and listen to the angriest music I can think of on my Walkman underneath the covers. After that, every time he walks into a room I am in, I make sure that I immediately walk out of it.

1998. I am fifteen, walking through the Northern Quarter in Manchester in my school uniform. A man shouts 'Hey schoolgirl!' to get my attention before asking me the time. After I tell him, he remarks that he's glad that I was wearing my uniform because otherwise he would have had to stop me by shouting 'Hey big tits!' I tell him to go fuck himself and storm off, trying not to cry. Trying not to feel the sting of shame under my skin.

***

An ex-boyfriend of mine once accused me of only seeing the world in black and white, when actually it was more in shades of grey. Obvious jokes aside, I sometimes feel he had a point. It's so simple to view things as either/or, right/wrong, simple/complicated when often, the reality of the situation is far more complex. Situations are nuanced, people never do the things you expect and bodies – and the people they belong to – are rarely what they seem.

I think of his words often when I see the discourse around bodies and how people should feel about them. I am a fat woman. I always have been and probably always will be. I spent most of my twenties hating my body and more time than I care to admit to in my thirties trying to make peace with it. I try to be an outspoken advocate of 'body positivity' and 'acceptance' and all those other buzzwords that people throw around nowadays. But all too often, I find these sentiments to be overly simplistic and trite, no matter how well-meaning they are.

'*Why do you hate your body?*' ask women with model bodies and tight abs, plus-size beauties with flat stomachs and breasts just the right size to be shunned by the traditional modelling industry but still considered attractive, still *acceptable*. Women who think it's brave to be photographed surrounded by packets of crisps as a 'daring rebuke to body shamers'.'*Look at my body*' they say. '*I don't hate my body. Why don't you stop hating yours? It's so easy to do! You should stop doing it. Why can't you stop doing it? Why can't you just flick that off switch in your head, Christina?*' Honestly. Do you not think I've tried?

There are days when the mere concept of 'body positivity' feels like magic, a spell that others can concoct but which I don't know the recipe for. I look at others who have performed the trick, pulled the rabbit out of the hat and long to get them to show me their secrets. I admire them openly, envy them privately, aspire to be them deeply. I think about what the excellent fat activist, Virgie Tovar, says about self love. How some days it is more difficult than others. That it can take years to master. That there is not a single, easy path to it and therefore you must become 'an engineer of that process'.

I am trying to get myself to the point where one day I look in the mirror and accept every aspect of my appearance. That's not to say that there aren't elements of myself that I admire. I love my arms, rippled with muscle and a multitude of bright tattoos – they can lift the weight of an adult man (in dumbbell form) over my head. I'm in continual awe of the firmness of my thighs and the soft cushion of my belly. I love to lie in bed in the morning and run my hands over the topography of myself, the dips and the swells, the warm wet caves, the delightful ripples. But when I reach my breasts... While I don't feel disgust, I don't exactly experience joy, either.

What I feel instead is something stranger, far more curdled and difficult. How can I dislike a part of my body that has defined who I am, the person I was and have become? I can't remember any point in my adult life where I've not been aware of my breasts, their size and how people have viewed me because of them.

***

2000. I am eighteen and working in my first bar job. I am required to wear a tight t-shirt. I tell a colleague that perhaps it would be easier for me to get a badge made saying 'MY TITS CAN'T POUR PINTS' for the benefit of every punter who attempts to order two pints of Kronenbourg from my chest.

2013. I am thirty, I am in a professional job that I am

proud of, where I am respected, and I overhear someone calling me 'Christina with the breasts', even though there was only one person with my name in my office. As if they are the only things I could ever be defined by.

A while ago. I am breaking up with a man who I have been sleeping with and who (unwisely) I have developed an unhealthy amount of feelings for. We are sitting in a restaurant and I am picking at a bowl of Bibimbap, trying to master my emotions, hold back the swell. After a few minutes of awkward silence, he says 'look, it's a good thing if we don't have sex anymore. After all, it's not like we really *fit*.' He looks at my chest and it take me a moment to realise that he's not talking about our emotional compatibility. I remember how, when we were fucking, my breasts squished awkwardly between our bodies. It had been bad sex and I remembered wondering at the time if mine was the largest pair he'd ever had to wrestle with. Maybe he was right. But it still hurt that he couldn't even be bothered trying to learn how we could make our bodies align. I take a deep breath and feel a fat tear roll down my cheek and into my unfinished dinner.

***

I am a woman of capacious appetites. For food. For books. For music. And for sex. And while I'd like to say that my breasts haven't had a part to play in influencing the latter, I've never been that good a liar.

People see a body like mine attached to the will of a woman like me and make assumptions. People who look at my husband and pronounce to him *'well, you must be a boob man!'* As though it is an either or. As though my breasts are twin sirens, luring him to me with their fleshy song, divorced completely from the woman attached to them. Her head, her heart.

The best sex I've ever had has been with people who know what to do with my body. Who are capable of manoeuvring it in ways that I – the one who should have mastery of it – could never begin to contemplate. Those who don't make me feel too outsized, but just right. Those people are rare, but when they've come into my life I've tried to appreciate them.

I always say that my favourite part of the day is when my husband joins me in bed and we wrap our arms around each other. I feel at my most complete when he sinks into my softness, the red thread that has forever tied us together growing slack in the face of our completeness. With him, I feel something that has all been all too rare sometimes. Enough.

***

2008. I am twenty-five and on my first date with the man who I will go on to marry. We have spent the day together in my flat in Manchester smoking, drinking whiskey and coke and listening to haunted sounding Radio 4 documentaries about numbers stations. Right now, we are lying naked on the floor of my bedroom as my landlord is yet to replace my curtains after fixing the broken window. (I've been hanging up my dresses in lieu of them, but I live on the ground floor so it's still a little too easy for passers-by to see everything going on.)

He rolls over and takes my breasts in his hands and suddenly I feel panicked. 'Sorry,' I say. 'I know they're very... large.'

There is a silence. 'Why are you embarrassed about them?'

'Because. They're just a lot. One of my exes said they were the size of former Soviet republics.'

'That's... exact.'

'We named them 'Kazakhstan and Uzbekistan.'

'Which one is which?'

'Lefty's Kazakhstan, Righty's Uzbekistan.'

He laughs at that, a laugh I will continue to love hearing for years, for decades, for the rest of my life.

'Just so you know, I think they're great.'

I blush.

'People will think you're a tit man, you know.'

'More fool them. I love tits and arses equally. Even more so when they're attached to someone bright and beautiful and funny.'

203

I am so used to my body being the punchline to a bad joke that I don't know how to respond to that. So I just lie there listening to the racing pulse of my heartbeat, feeling the rough carpet beneath my back, looking into the eyes of this person who sees me for what I am and think 'Finally.'

***

People have always told me that I'm remarkably hard on myself. That comparing myself to other talents, other bodies, will only make me miserable. And I am gradually waking up to more and more mornings where I am able to wear my body lightly. Where it feels as though it fits, like it could nestle easily in the crook of an elbow. At times like this, my breasts feel like what they are. Soft. Safe. Normal. I feel a tenderness towards them that has long been absent when I look at them in the mirror. It is possible for me to appreciate their softness and value the warmth that comes from shoving my hands underneath them on cold, lonely nights away from home.

So, perhaps it's time to call a truce on the war I have been waging against myself so long. While 'love' is too strong a word for what I feel about my breasts, I hope that one day I will be able to pin it to my chest and wear it with pride. But I will always fly their flag. I will always be their champion. After all, they're the only tits I'll ever have.

Side Effects
Rebecca Thursten

headache

headache ibuprofen not working

headache migraine difference

migraine cluster headache difference

caffeine bad headache

caffeine good headache

alcohol good headache

[...]

headache insomnia

headache insomnia anxiety

insomnia alcohol

[...]

drowning nightmare

nightmare can't move

night paralysis

night terrors

night terrors in art

night terrors real

night terrors ghosts

night terrors alcohol

[...]

sleep sweat

wake up sweating

sweat composition

sweat salt

wake up skin sore

[...]

nausea

antiemetic drugs

natural household antiemetics

vomit nothing coming up

vomit tastes like salt

[...]

blurred vision

blurred vision eyes hurt to open

conjunctivitis

conjunctivitis eye gunk

eye gunk composition

eye gunk salt

[...]

psychosomatic illness

screen light bad for you

limit screen time

screen light can't sleep

internet loneliness health

salt damage keyboard

[...]

salt mythology

salt witches

salt holy

blessed salt

cursed salt

dead sea

fresh water

bodies of fresh water near n22

[...]

why do songs get stuck in your head

"i'm gonna suck the salt off your teeth" lyrics

"suck the salt off your teeth" lyrics

"suck the salt of your teeth" lyrics

"suck the salt" lyrics

aural hallucination

[...]

salt hair

salt nails

salt throat

salt thoughts

[...]

dehydration

dehydration side effects

rehydration

how much water can a person drink

how to drink a lot of water at once

drinking lots of water dangerous

water intoxication

how much water will kill you exact

why won't you help me why won't you help me you never even had a body you don't know what a body is you don't know a fucking thing you don't know the difference between a letter and the finger that pushes the key your skin has never cracked you've never bled you've never felt a fucking thing you aren't afraid to fucking die you never even lived fuck you fuck you fuck you fuck you don't care about me you don't care about me you don't fucking care

[...]

water damage macbook

Our Authors & Artists

Michael Amherst is a writer and critic. His debut book on truth and desire through the frame of bisexuality, *Go the Way Your Blood Beats*, is published by Repeater Books. His short fiction has appeared in publications including *The White Review* and *Contrappasso* and has been longlisted for BBC Opening Lines and the Bath Short Story Prize, and shortlisted for the Bridport Prize. His essays and reviews have appeared in the *Guardian*, *New Statesman*, *Attitude* and *The London Magazine*, among others. He is a recipient of an award from Arts Council England and is currently working on a novel as part of a PhD at Birkbeck, University of London.

Marta Bausells is a writer and editor living in London. Her writing has appeared in the *New York Times Magazine*, the *Guardian*, the *Observer*, *Literary Review*, *The Millions* and *Electric Literature*, among others. She has been awarded an inaugural London Writers Award for Non-Fiction (2018). She is also literary editor at *ELLE UK*, European editor-at-large at *Literary Hub*, and a contributing editor at *Oh Comely* magazine, and runs the London chapter of Subway Book Review. She has recently spent time in Berlin on a fellowship from the International Journalists Programme. Previously she worked for *Guardian Books*, where she founded the Guardian Books Network. She tweets at @martabausells.

Stephanie Boland has written for the *New Statesman*, *Asymptote*, *LA Review of Books* and *Prospect*. She has a doctorate in modernist literature and lives in South London.

Sami Çapulcu is a mathematician and amateur science nerd. To date, most of her writing has been for zines and compact political flyers. She is an organiser around anti-racist and queer struggles, and plans/facilitates workshops rather than sleeping.

Jake Elliott is a writer. He lives in London.

Cara English is an Irish anti-poverty and trans campaigner, as well as occasional chef. Her work is concerned with what constitutes the feminine under late-stage capitalism, and what role government plays in bringing about bodily dignity. You can read more about her current campaigning with Gendered Intelligence, or her new project to map out all gender-neutral loos in the UK at open lavs.

Livia Franchini is a writer and translator from Tuscany, Italy. Selected publications include *The Quietus, 3:AM, The White Review, LESTE, Hotel, PEN Transmissions* and the anthologies *On Bodies* (3 of Cups Press) and *Wretched Strangers* (Boiler House Press). She has translated Natalia Ginzburg, James Tiptree Jr. and Michael Donaghy among many others. Livia is one of the inaugural writers-in-residence from the Connecting Emerging Literary Artist project, funded by the European Union, which will see her work translated into six languages. She has performed her work internationally, most notably at Faber Social, Standon Calling, Lowlands and the Hay Festival. Livia is currently at work on her first novel, as part of a funded PhD in experimental women's writing at Goldsmiths, University of London.

Clouds Haberberg is a queer London-based, half-Italian writer and musician. They've spent the last several years ranting about disability and mental illness on the Internet, and they've finally managed to channel some of that energy into their first published essay here.

Rosie Haward is a writer and podcaster based between Hastings and Amsterdam, where she recently completed an MA in Critical Studies at the Sandberg Instituut. As well as writing about bodies, queerness and the sea, together with Matty Hemming she co-writes and presents the podcast Textual Feelings, which focuses on genre-bending, queer and feminist books. To see more of her work visit www.rosiehaward.info and www.textual-feelings.tumblr.com.

Rachel Heng's debut novel, *Suicide Club*, will be translated in nine languages worldwide and has been featured as a most anticipated read by *The Independent, The Irish Times, The Huffington Post, Gizmodo, ELLE, Grazia, Stylist* and *NYLON*. Her short fiction has received a Pushcart Prize Special Mention and Prairie Schooner's Jane Geske Award, and has been published in *Glimmer Train, The Offing, Prairie Schooner* and elsewhere. Rachel is currently a fellow at the Michener Center for Writers, University of Texas at Austin.

Krish Jeyakumar is a British-Tamil creative, born and bred in East London. They have a degree in English, a passion for photography and spend most of their time researching, writing and dreaming about Hindu Vedic literature. Most of their work is based around their experience as a gender confused, androgynous brown person. They can be found wandering around thinking about Kali, looking for leaves to press, or more conveniently on Twitter.

Ana Kinsella is an Irish writer in London.

Umairah Malik is a freelance writer, mental health activist and bookworm. She is the blog editor for literary magazine *Salomé* and has written for various publications. Follow her on twitter at @umairah_x.

Rica March is a comic artist from Stockholm, Sweden. She enjoys working in a variety of genres, but especially likes to focus on queer representation in historical settings. Her work has been part of several comic anthologies, most notably *Beyond 2: The Queer Comic Anthology* by Beyond Press. You can find more of her work on her website: www.poppyapples.net/

Christina McDermott is a writer living in Liverpool. She was born in Manchester in 1982 and graduated with a BA in History from University College London in 2004. Her work has been featured in the *Guardian, Independent, Washington Post,* BBC, *NME* and *The Pool* among others and she runs the social media agency Cattington. She tweets at @christinamcmc.

Kiran Millwood Hargrave is an award-winning poet, and bestselling author of *The Girl of Ink & Stars*, which won the British Children's Book of the Year, and the Waterstones Children's Book Prize 2017, and *The Island at the End of Everything*, which won the Historical Association Young Quills Award, and was shortlisted for the Costa Book Awards, and the Blue Peter Award. Her forthcoming books include *The Way Past Winter* (Chicken House, 2018), and her debut novel for adults, *The Mercies* (Picador, 2020).

Kasim Mohammed is a 23-year-old writer based in Nottinghamshire. He works as an editorial assistant during the day and as a critic on culture to anyone who will listen at night. He is currently working on several writing projects (far too many to handle) and aspires to make the publishing industry as colourful as possible, starting with himself.

S. Niroshini is a Sri Lankan-born writer and odissi dancer. Her work engages with themes of gender, cultural history, migration and memory. Her poetry, essays and criticism have been seen on Bedtime Stories for the End of the World, *Wasafiri* and City of Stories. She lives in London. @_nishasoma

Stephanie Phillips is a London-based arts & culture journalist. She is also a member of black feminist punk band Big Joanie. Her work has been featured in outlets such as Noisey, Bandcamp, and *Alternative Press*. She contributed an essay to the 2017 anthology *Under My Thumb: Songs that Hate Women and the Women Who Love Them* edited by Rhian E. Jones and Eli Davies. She also contributed several essays to *Women Who Rock*, edited by Evelyn McDonnell. You can follow her on Twitter @stephanopolus or read more of her work here: steph-phillips.com.

Ari Potter is a Bengali-British writer who's particulary interested in gender, mental health and cultural identity. She's previously appeared in *gal-dem, Orlando* and *Litro*. By day, she works for a health and social care charity, and, separately, has recently launched her own campaign on consent and sex education.

215

Aki Schilz is a Queen's Ferry Press Finalist (Best Small Fictions), and has been featured in the Wigleaf Top 50. She was the winner of the inaugural Visual Verse Prize, and the Bare Fiction Prize for Flash Fiction 2014. Her writing appears in print (inc. *Synaesthesia Magazine, Year's Best Weird Fiction IV, Popshot, An Unreliable Guide to London*) and online (inc. The Bohemyth, Cheap Pop Lit, The Vagina Project, And Other Poems). She is co-founder of the #LossLit project, a judge for the Bridport Prize and Creative Future Literary Awards for marginalised writers, and Director of The Literary Consultancy.

Alice Tarbuck is a writer and PhD candidate in innovative poetics and environmental humanities at the Scottish Poetry Library and Dundee University. Recent publications include essays for *Nasty Women* by 404 Ink and *The Bi-ble* by Monstrous Regiment. She has poetry published in *Zarf, Datableed Zine, Antiphon* and others, and was recently shortlisted for the Jupiter Artland Poetry Prize.

Rebecca Thursten is a British writer based in Brooklyn. She is working on a PhD at NYU and is trying to spend less time on the internet. She can be found on the internet, tweeting from @tacceber.

Bryony White is a LAHP-funded PhD student at King's College London. She writes on performance and contemporary art. Her writing has been featured in *Frieze, the Los Angeles Review of Books, ArtMonthly* and the *TLS*. She co-edits the monthly TinyLetter, close and is currently working on her first novel. She tweets at @bryonylwhite.

Acknowledgements

This book would not have been possible without the talent and hard work of our contributors and the generous pledges via Kickstarter. We would like to give special thanks to the following people:

Ian Abbott
Madeline Adeane
Kate Ahl
J. Alexander
Alex Allison
Jane Amherst
Michael Amherst
Amy Ashenden
Melanie Ashford
Ant Attwood
Colette Auer
Caden Bågenholm
Sarah Balmont
James Barlow
Jonathan Bay
Leanne Bell
Jennifer Bernstein
Alice Bogen
Daniel Bogen
Rachel Bogen Otero
Sally Bonneywell
Isabel Branco
Ruth Bridget Brennan
Matt Bridgeman-Rivett
Siobhan Britton
Nell Brown
D Bubulj
Matt Button
Naomi Byrne
Sophie Campbell
Elsa Carron
Sarah Carter

Ollie Chamberlain
Malcolm Chisholm
Christopher Churches-Lindsay
LC Clarke
Yvonne Clarke-Salt
Tom Clayton
Mikaella Clements
Dr. Kay K. Clopton
Jo Crispin
Theodora Danek
Jim Dean
Will Dean
Lucie Elliott
Lori England
Alan Evans
Madeleine Fenner
Alice Field
Matthew Flanagan
Emma Flynn
Hannah "Er00" Fordham
Nicole Froio
Aisling Gallagher
Lesley Gane
Sarah Garnham
Dian Maisie Otter Grace
Rob Gregg
Adrian Haberberg
Paul Hancock
Daniel Hahn
Theresa M. Hahn
Jamie Rose Hathaway
Sharon Haward

Gem Hill

Erin Himrod

Tomasz Hoskins

Mischa How

Sally Huband

Bex Hughes

Siân Hunter

Dan Hutchins

Graham Huws

Laura Huxley

Naadir Jeewa

Krisanthi Jeyakumar

Beth John

Tanya MB Johnson

Keith & Aliy Jones

Laura Joyce

Lucy Kelsall

Karolina Klermon-Williams

Katherine E. Knotts

Nathaniel Kunitsky

Patrick Langley

Fion J. Lau

Gayle Lazda

Cathy Leech

Danni Lutts

Chelle M

Katherine Mackinnon

Sophie Mackintosh

Esmee Maltby

Kuukuwa Manful

Kevin Maxwell

Rachel May

Fahad Mayet

Christina McDermott-McGarrigle (McMc)

Superior Alex McDonald

Pete McGee

Emer McHugh

Marie-Anne McQuay

Anne Meadows

Elle Meggs

Fay Myers

Angelique Neumann

Christina Neuwirth

Moose D Ofdensen

Emily Oram

Susie P

Ajay Patel

Thomas Peacock

Jane and Martin Pennington

Naomi Pennington

Will Pollard

Alex Primavesi

Maggie Primavesi

Alexa Radcliffe-Hart

Parvati Rajamani

Jennifer Rainbow

Laura Renshaw

Will Rees

Hannah Riviere Scott

Chris and Cathy Roberts

Eloise Roberts

Charlie Rodgers

Matthew J. Rogers

Hannah Ross

Kurt Schleier

Hazel Nico Shaw

Shelley Shocolinsky-Dwyer

Ollie Simpson

Julie Siwicki

Sam Steddy

Alice Stringer

Zeba Talkhani

Sharlene Teo

Josie Thaddeus-Johns

Laura and Bryan Thomas

Pen Thompson

Georgie Thurlby
Janet Titchener
Hannah Trevarthen
Claire Trévien
Tori Truslow
Clemens Uittenbosch
Abbie Vickress
Samantha Walton
Sami Wannell
Robin White
Mark Whitehead
Claire Williams
Pip Williams
Tim Williams
Catherine Williamson
Jenn Williamson
Ben Winston
Andrew Woods
Sarah Woolley
Sarah Wray
Jill Y
Katrina Zaat
Oscar Zhang-Borges
Dani (@dani_reviews)
Ash
Jeton
KS
PhilithD

Dead Ink Books
Illumicrate
Sad Press

Creating a book is a team effort, and 3 of Cups Press would like to thank everyone who helped bring *On Bodies* from manuscript to published book.

Clare Bogen
Ka Bradley
Sophie Campbell
Anna Coatman
Lisa Goodrum
Lizzie Huxley-Jones
Vanessa Peterson
Cornelia Prior
Fran Roberts
Harriet Smelt